CAP 413

RADIOTELEPHONY MANUAL

CIVIL AVIATION AUTHORITY LONDON AUGUST 1992

© Civil Aviation Authority 1992

ISBN 0 86039 510 3

First published September 1978
Reprinted January 1979
Reprinted October 1979
Second edition April 1984
Reprinted September 1984
Reprinted with corrections June 1986
Reprinted September 1987
Reprinted January 1989
Reprinted December 1989
Reprinted with corrections September 1990
Reprinted July 1991
Reprinted January 1992
Third edition August 1992

Printed and distributed by
Civil Aviation Authority, Greville House, 37 Gratton Road, Cheltenham, England

FOREWORD

STATUS

This publication is based on the International Standards and Recommended Practices contained in ICAO Annex 10 Volume 2 (Communications Procedures) to the Convention on International Civil Aviation and the PANS-RAC (Procedures for Air Navigation Services, Rules of the Air and Air Traffic Services) Doc 4444 – RAC5.01.11.

It is a useful reference book for the examination for the Flight Radiotelephony Operator's (Restricted) Licence. Current operational details are to be found in the United Kingdom AIP, however, air traffic controllers, aerodrome flight information officers and aeronautical radio station operators should refer to MATS Pt 1, MAFIS (CAP 410) and Operators' Guide (CAP 452) respectively for comprehensive instructions on phraseology to be used by aeronautical ground radio stations.

RTF changes detailed in this revision become effective on 28 September 1992. Major changes to RTF phraseology will be notified in Aeronautical Information Circulars (AICs); updated versions of this Manual will be published at regular intervals. Users of this manual who do not already have access to AICs may wish to consider subscribing to the AIC Amendment Service in order to maintain the currency of this publication. Details of this service may be obtained from the CAA at the address shown in the Bibliography at page 165.

FORMAT

The examples of phraseology in this handbook are intended to be representative of radiotelephony procedures in common use. The initial call in a series of messages in Chapters 2–11 inclusive always appear on the left hand side of the page; remaining messages connected with the subject of the initial call appear in chronological order on the right hand side.

The agency making the transmission is identified by the colour background of the example phraseology as follows:

AIRCRAFT

GROUND STATION (ATC, AFIS, A/G)

VEHICLE

While the procedures and phraseologies specifically reflect the situation in an environment where Very High Frequency (VHF) is in use, they are equally applicable in those areas where High Frequency (HF) is used. In the latter case a strict adherence to procedures is considered essential because of the greater interference potential and in many cases poor reception resulting from the propagation characteristics of certain frequency bands.

All enquiries regarding the text of this publication should be addressed to:

Head of AP3
Room T1027
CAA House
45–59 Kingsway
London WC2B 6TE

TABLE OF CONTENTS

CHAPTER 1 – GLOSSARY

1.1 DEFINITIONS

Aerodrome   Any area of land or water designed, equipped, set apart or commonly used for affording facilities for the landing and departure of aircraft.

Aerodrome Control Service   Air traffic control service for aerodrome traffic.

Aerodrome Traffic   All traffic on the manoeuvring area of an aerodrome and all aircraft operating in the vicinity of an aerodrome.

Aerodrome Mobile Service   A radio communication service between aircraft stations and aeronautical stations, or between aircraft stations.

Aeronautical Station   A land station in the aeronautical mobile service. In certain instances, an aeronautical station may be placed on board a ship or an earth satellite.

Aircraft Station   A mobile station in the aeronautical mobile service on board an aircraft.

Air-ground Communications   Two-way communication between aircraft and stations or locations on the surface of the earth.

Air Traffic   All aircraft in flight or operating on the manoeuvring area of an aerodrome.

Air Traffic Control Centre   A term used in the United Kingdom to describe a unit providing en-route air traffic control services.

Air Traffic Control Clearance   Authorisation for an aircraft to proceed under conditions specified by an air traffic control unit.

Air Traffic Services (ATS)   A generic term meaning variously, flight information service, alerting service, air traffic advisory service, air traffic control service, area control service, approach control service or aerodrome control service.

Airway   A control area or part of a control area established in the form of a corridor equipped with radio navigation aids.

Altitude The vertical distance of a level, a point or an object considered as a point, measured from mean sea level.

Automatic Terminal Information Service (ATIS) The provision of current, routine information to arriving and departing aircraft by means of continuous and repetitive broadcasts throughout the day or a specified portion of the day.

Blind Transmission A transmission from one station to another station in circumstances where two-way communication cannot be established but where it is believed that the called station is able to receive the transmission.

Broadcast A transmission of information relating to air navigation that is not addressed to a specific station or stations.

Clearance Limit The point to which an aircraft is granted an air traffic control clearance.

Control Area A controlled airspace extending upwards from a specified limit above the surface of the earth.

Controlled Airspace An airspace of defined dimensions within which air traffic control service is provided to IFR flights and to VFR flights in accordance with the airspace classification.

Control Zone A controlled airspace extending upwards from the surface of the earth to a specified upper limit.

Decision Height A specified height in a precision approach at which a missed approach must be initiated if the required visual referene to continue the approach to land has not been established.

Elevation The vertical distance of a point or level on, or affixed to, the surface of the earth measured from mean sea level.

Estimated Time of Arrival The time at which the pilot estimates that the aircraft will be over a specific location.

Flight Level A surface of constant atmospheric pressure, which is related to a specific pressure datum, 1013.2 mb, and is separated from other such surfaces by specific pressure intervals.

Flight Plan   Specified information provided to air traffic services units, relative to an intended flight or portion of a flight of an aircraft. Flight Plans fall into two categories: Full Flight Plans and Abbreviated Flight Plans.

General Air Traffic   Flights operating in accordance with civil air traffic cprocedures.

Heading   The direction in which the longitudinal axis of an aircraft is pointed, usually expressed in degrees from North (magnetic).

Height   The vertical distance of a level, a point, or an object considered as a point measured from a specified datum.

IFR Flight   A flight conducted in accordance with the instrument flight rules.

Instrument Meteorological Conditions (IMC)   Meteorological conditions expressed in terms of visibility, horizontal and vertical distance from cloud, less than the minima specified for visual meteorological conditions.

Known Traffic   Traffic, the current flight details and intentions of which are known to the controller concerned through direct communication or co-ordination.

Level   A generic term relating to the vertical position of an aircraft in flight and meaning variously, height, altitude or flight level.

Minimum Descent Height   A height in a non-precision or circling approach below which descent may not be made without visual reference.

Missed Approach Procedure (MAP)   The procedure to be followed if the approach cannot be continued.

Radar Vectoring   Provision of navigational guidance to aircraft in the form of specific headings, based on the use of radar.

Reporting Point   A specified geographical location in relation to which the position of an aircraft can be reported.

Runway Visual Range   The range over which the pilot of an aircraft on the centre line of a runway can expect to see the runway surface markings, or the lights delineating the runway or identifying its centre line.

VFR Flight   A flight conducted in accordance with the visual flight rules.

Visual Meteorological Conditions (VMC)   Meteorological conditions expressed in terms of visibility, horizontal and vertical distance from cloud, equal to or better than specified minima.

1.2   COMMONLY USED ABBREVIATIONS

1.2.1   The abbreviations annotated with an asterisk are normally spoken as complete words. The remainder are normally spoken using the constituent letters rather than the spelling alphabet.

A

aal	Above Aerodrome Level
ADF	Automatic Direction-Finding Equipment
ADR	Advisory Route
ADT	Approved Departure Time
AFIS*	Aerodrome Flight Information Service
AFTN	Aeronautical Fixed Telecommunication Network
AGL	Above Ground Level
AIC	Aeronautical Information Circular
AIP	Aeronautical Information Publication
AIS	Aeronautical Information Services
amsl	Above Mean Sea Level
ANO	Air Navigation Order
ATA	Actual Time of Arrival
ATC	AIr Traffic Control (in general)
ATCC	Air Traffic Control Centre
ATD	Actual Time of Departure
ATIS*	Automatic Terminal Information Service
ATS	Air Traffic Service
ATSU	Air Traffic Services Unit
ATZ	Aerodrome Traffic Zone

C

CAA	Civil Aviation Authority
CAVOK*	Visibility, cloud and present weather better than prescribed values or conditions (CAVOK pronounced Cav-okay)
CTA	Control Area
CTR	Control Zone

D

DAAIS*	Danger Area Activity Information Service (DAAIS pronounced DAY-ES)
DACS	Danger Area Crossing Service
DF	Direction Finding
DME	Distance Measuring Equipment

E

EAT	Expected Approach Time
ETA	Estimated Time of Arrival
ETD	Estimated Time of Departure

F

FAF	Final Approach Fix
FIR	Flight Information Region
FIS	Flight Information Service
FL	Flight Level
ft	Foot (feet)

G

GAT	General Air Traffic
GMC	Ground Movement Control

H

H24	Continuous day and night service (H24 pronounced Aitch Twenty Fower)
HF	High Frequency
HJ	Sunrise to Sunset

I

ICAO	International Civil Aviation Organisation
IFR	Instrument Flight Rules
ILS	Instrument Landing System
IMC	Instrument Meteorological Conditions

K

kt	Knots

M

MATZ*	Military Aerodrom e Traffic Zone
MET*	Meteorological or Meteorology
METAR*	Routine aviation aerodrome weather report
mb	Millibars

N

NATS   National Air Traffic Services
NDB   Non-Directional Radio Beacon

O

OAC   Oceanic Area Control Unit
OCA   Oceanic Control Area

P

PAPIS*   Precision Approach Path Indicating System (PAPIS pronounced Pa-pee)

Q

QDM   Magnetic heading (zero wind) (Sometimes employed to indicate magnetic heading of a runway)
QDR   Magnetic bearing
QFE   The observed pressure at a specified datum (usually aerodrome or runway threshold elevation) corrected for temperature
QGH   Ground interpreted letdown procedure using DF equipment
QNH   Altimeter sub-scale setting to obtain elevation when on the ground and indications of elevation when in the air
QTE   True Bearing

R

RCC   Rescue Co-ordination Centre
RTF   Radiotelephone/Radiotelephony
RVR*   Runway Visual Range

S

SAR   Search and Rescue
SID*   Standard Instrument Departure
SIGMET* Significant information concerning en-route weather phenomena which may affect the safety of aircraft operations
SRA   Surveillance Radar Approach
SSR   Secondary Surveillance Radar
STAR*   Standard (instrument) Arrival Route

T

TAF*	Terminal Aerodrome Forecast
TMA	Terminal Control Area

U

UHF	Ultra-High Frequency
UIR	Upper Flight Information Region
UTC	Co-ordinated Universal Time

V

VASIS*	Visual Approach Slope Indicator System (VASIS pronounced Var-zi)
VDF	Very High Frequency Direction-Finding Station
VFR	Visual Flight Rules
VHF	Very High Frequency (30 to 300 MHz)
VMC	Visual Meteorological Conditions
VOLMET*	Meteorological information for aircraft in flight
VOR	VHF Omnidirectional Radio Range
VORTAC*	VOR and TACAN combination

1.3   HOURS OF SERVICE AND COMMUNICATIONS WATCH

1.3.1   The hours of service of the radio facilities available in the United Kingdom are published in the UK AIP (COM 2) which also details those periods set aside for maintenance.

1.3.2   When an aircraft has established communication with an ATSU it is required to maintain a listening watch with that ATSU and advise the ATSU when the listening watch is about to cease. Aircraft will not cease to maintain a listening watch, except for reasons of safety, without informing the ATSU concerned. A time at which it is expected that the watch will be resumed must be stated.

1.4   RECORD OF COMMUNICATIONS

1.4.1   An aircraft telecommunication log-book is not required to be kept in respect of communication by radiotelephony with an aeronautical station which provides a radio service for aircraft. Many UK aeronautical stations have automatic recording equipment for air-ground communications but at those which do not a record is kept of all communications with aircraft.

1.5   CATEGORIES OF MESSAGE

1.5.1   The categories of messages handled by the aeronautical mobile service are in the following order of priority:

(a)   Distress messages

(b)   Urgency messages

See Chapter 9 – Emergency RTF Procedures

(c)   Communications relating to direction finding

(d)   Flight safety messages   See Chapter 7 para 11.6

(e)   Meteorological messages

(f)   Flight Regularity messages   See Chapter 11 para 11.6

CHAPTER 2 – GENERAL OPERATING PROCEDURES

2.1 INTRODUCTION

2.1.1 Radiotelephony provides the means by which pilots and ground personnel communicate with each other. Used properly, the information and instructions transmitted are of vital importance in assisting in the safe and expeditious operation of aircraft. However, the use of non-standard procedures and phraseology can cause misunderstanding. Incidents and accidents have occurred in which a contributing factor has been the misunderstanding caused by the use of non-standard phraseology. *The importance of using correct and precise standard phraseology cannot be over-emphasised.*

2.2 TRANSMITTING TECHNIQUE

2.2.1 The following transmitting techniques will assist in ensuring that transmitted speech is clearly and satisfactorily received.

   (a) Before transmitting check that the receiver volume is set at the optimum level and listen out on the frequency to be used to ensure that there will be no interference with a transmission from another station.

   (b) Be familiar with microphone operating techniques and do not turn your head away from it whilst talking or vary the distance between it and your mouth. Severe distortion of speech may arise from:

   (i) talking too close to the microphone

   (ii) touching the microphone with the lips

   (iii) holding the microphone or boom (of a combined headset/microphone system).

   (c) Use a normal conversation tone, speak clearly and distinctly.

   (d) Maintain an even rate of speech not exceeding 100 words per minute. When it is known that elements of the message will be written down by the recipients, speak at a slightly slower rate.

   (e) Maintain the speaking volume at a constant level.

(f)   A slight pause before and after numbers will assist in making them easier to understand.

(g)   Avoid using hesitation sounds such as 'er'.

(h)   Depress the transmit switch fully before speaking and do not release it until the message is complete. This will ensure that the entire message is transmitted. However, do not depress transmit switch until ready to speak.

(i)   Be aware that the mother tongue of the person receiving the message may not be English. Therefore, speak clearly and use standard radiotelephony (RTF) words and phrases wherever possible.

2.2.2   One of the most irritating and potentially dangerous situations in radiotelephony is a 'stuck' microphone button. Operators should always ensure that the button is released after a transmission and the microphone placed in an appropriate place that will ensure that it will not inadvertently be switched on.

2.3   TRANSMISSION OF LETTERS

2.3.1   The words in the table below shall be used when individual letters are required to be transmitted. The syllables to be emphasised are underlined.

Letter	Word	Appropriate pronunciation
A	Alpha	AL FAH
B	Bravo	BRAH VOH
C	Charlie	CHAR LEE
D	Delta	DELL TAH
E	Echo	ECK OH
F	Foxtrot	FOKS TROT
G	Golf	GOLF
H	Hotel	HOH TELL

Letter	Word	Appropriate pronunciation
I	India	IN DEE AH
J	Juliett	JEW LEE ETT
K	Kilo	KEY LOH
L	Lima	LEE MAH
M	Mike	MIKE
N	November	NO VEM BER
O	Oscar	OSS CAH
P	Papa	PAH PAH
Q	Quebec	KEH BECK
R	Romeo	ROW ME OH
S	Sierra	SEE AIR RAH
T	Tango	TANG GO
U	Uniform	YOU NEE FORM
V	Victor	VIK TAH
W	Whiskey	WISS KEY
X	X-ray	ECKS RAY
Y	Yankee	YANG KEE
Z	Zulu	ZOO LOO

2.4 TRANSMISSION OF NUMBERS

2.4.1 The syllables to be emphasised are underlined.

Numeral or numeral element	Latin alphabet representation
0	ZERO
1	WUN
2	TOO

Numeral or numeral element	Latin alphabet representation
3	TREE
4	FOWER
5	FIFE
6	SIX
7	SEVEN
8	AIT
9	NINER
Decimal	DAYSEEMAL
Hundred	HUN DRED
Thousand	TOUSAND

2.4.2   All numbers except whole hundreds, whole thousands and combinations of thousands and whole hundreds shall be transmitted by pronouncing each digit separately. Whole hundreds and whole thousands shall be transmitted by pronouncing each digit in the number of hundreds or thousands followed by the word HUNDRED or THOUSAND as appropriate. Combinations of thousands and whole hundreds shall be transmitted by pronouncing each digit in the number of thousands followed by the word THOUSAND and the number of hundreds followed by the word HUNDRED.

Number	Transmitted as	Pronounced as
10	One Zero	WUN ZERO
75	Seven Five	SEVEN FIFE
100	One Hundred	WUN HUN DRED
583	Five Eight Three	FIFE AIT TREE
2 500	Two Thousand Five Hundred	TOO TOUSAND FIFE HUNDRED
11 000	One One Thousand	WUN WUN TOUSAND
25 000	Two Five Thousand	TOO FIFE TOUSAND
38 143	Three Eight One Four Three	TREE AIT WUN FOWER TREE

12

2.4.3 Numbers containing a decimal point shall be transmitted as prescribed in 2.4.1 with the decimal point in appropriate sequence being indicated by the word decimal.

Number	Transmitted as	Pronounced as
118.1	One One Eight Decimal One	WUN WUN AIT DAY SEE MAL WUN
120.375	One Two Zero Decimal Three Seven	WUN TOO ZERO DAY SEE MAL TREE SEVEN

Note: Only the first five figures are used when identifying frequencies separated by 25 kHz.

2.4.4 When it is necessary to verify the accurate reception of numbers the person transmitting the message shall request the person receiving the message to read back the numbers.

2.5 TRANSMISSION OF TIME

2.5.1 When transmitting time, only the minutes of the hour are normally required. However, the hour should be included if there is any possibility of confusion. Time checks shall be given to the nearest minute. Co-ordinated Universal Time (UTC) is to be used at all times, unless specified. 2400 hours designates midnight, the end of the day, and 0000 hours the beginning of the day.

Number	Transmitted as	Pronounced as
0823	Two Three or Zero Eight Two Three	TOO TREE (or ZERO AIT TOO TREE)
1300	One Three Zero Zero	WUN TREE ZERO ZERO
2057	Five Seven or Two Zero Five Seven	FIFE SEVEN (or TOO ZERO FIFE SEVEN)

2.6 STANDARD WORDS AND PHRASES

2.6.1 The following words and phrases shall be used in radiotelephony communications as appropriate and shall have the meaning given below:

Word/Phrase	Meaning
ACKNOWLEDGE	Let me know that you have received and understood this message.
AFFIRM	Yes
APPROVED	Permission for proposed action granted.
BREAK	Indicates the separation between messages.
CANCEL	Annul the previously transmitted clearance.
CHANGING TO	I intend to call . . . (unit) on . . . (frequency)
CHECK	Examine a system or procedure (no answer is normally expected).
CLEARED	Authorised to proceed under the conditions specified.
CLIMB	Climb and maintain
CONFIRM	Have I correctly received the following ...? or Did you correctly receive this message?
CONTACT	Establish radio contact with ... (your details have been passed)
CORRECT	That is correct.
CORRECTION	An error has been made in this transmission (or message indicated). The correct version is ...
DESCEND	Descend and maintain
DISREGARD	Consider that transmission as not sent.
FREECALL	Call . . . (unit) (your details have not been passed – mainly used by military ATC)
HOW DO YOU READ	What is the readability of my transmission.
I SAY AGAIN	I repeat for clarity or emphasis.
MONITOR	Listen out on (frequency).

Word/Phrase	Meaning
NEGATIVE	No or Permission not granted or That is not correct.
OVER	My transmission is ended and I expect a response from you.
OUT	This exchange of transmissions is ended and no response is expected.
PASS YOUR MESSAGE	Proceed with your message.
READ BACK	Repeat all, or the specified part, of this message back to me exactly as received.
REPORT	Pass requested information.
REQUEST	I should like to know ... or I wish to obtain ...
ROGER	I have received all your last transmission. *Note: Under no circumstances to be used in reply to a question requiring a direct answer in the affirmative (AFFIRM) or negative (NEGATIVE).*
SAY AGAIN	Repeat all, or the following part of your last transmission.
SPEAK SLOWER	Reduce your rate of speech.
STANDBY	Wait and I will call you. *Note: No onward clearance to be assumed.*
VERIFY	Check and confirm.
WILCO	I understand your message and will comply with it (abbreviation for will comply)
WORDS TWICE	*As a request:* Communication is difficult. Please send every word twice. *As Information:* Since communication is difficult, every word in this message will be sent twice.

2.7 COMMUNICATIONS

2.7.1 Callsigns for aeronautical stations

2.7.1.1 Aeronautical stations are identified by the name of the location followed by a suffix. The suffix indicates the type of service being provided.

Service	Suffix
Area Control Service	CONTROL
Radar (in general)	RADAR
Approach Control	APPROACH
Aerodrome Control	TOWER
Ground Movement Control	GROUND
Precision Approach Radar	TALKDOWN (Military – FINAL CONTROLLER)
Flight Information Service	INFORMATION
Aerodrome Air/Ground Communications Service	RADIO
Ground Movement Planning	DELIVERY

2.7.1.2 There are three main categories of aeronautical communications service:

Air traffic control service (ATC) which can only be provided by licensed air traffic controllers who are closely regulated by the CAA.

Aerodrome flight information service (AFIS) which can be provided only be licensed aerodrome flight information service officers (AFISOs) who are mainly self-regulating.

Aerodrome air/ground communications service (A/G) which can be provided by radio operations who are not licensed but have obtained a certificate of competency to operate radio equipment on aviation frequencies from the CAA. These operations come under the jurisdiction of the radio license holder, but are not regulated in any other way.

It is an offence to use a callsign for a purpose other than that for which it has been notified.

2.7.1.3   When satisfactory communication has been established, and provided that it will *not be confusing*, the name of the location or the callsign suffix may be omitted.

2.7.2   Aircraft Callsigns

2.7.2.1   When establishing communication an aircraft shall use the full callsigns of both stations.

> Borton Tower G-ABCD   G-ABCD Borton Tower

2.7.2.2   After satisfactory communication has been established and provided that no confusion is likely to occur, the ground station may abbreviate callsigns (see table below). A pilot may *only* abbreviate the callsign of his aircraft if it has *first* been abbreviated by the aeronautical ground station.

Type	Example	
	Full	*Abbreviated*
(a) the five-character callsign corresponding to the registration marking of the aircraft;	G-ABCD	G-CD
(b) the five-character callsign referred to in (a) above, preceded by the radiotelephony designator of the aircraft operating agency;	AIR CANADA CFCAD	AIR CANADA AD
(c) the five-character callsign referred to in (a) above, preceded by the type of the aircraft;	SLINGSBY G-ABCD	SLINGSBY CD
(d) the radiotelephony designator of the aircraft operating agency, followed by the flight identification;	SPEEDBIRD 725	no abbreviation permitted
(e) the characters corresponding to the registration marking of the aircraft.	N357826	N826

2.7.2.3 An aircraft should request the service required on initial contact when freecalling a ground station.

> Westbury Approach, G-ABCD request Lower Airspace Radar Service

> Wrayton Control, G-ABCD I wish to file an airborne flight plan

2.7.2.4 An aircraft shall not change its callsign type during a flight. *However*, where there is a likelihood that confusion may occur because of similar callsigns, an aircraft may be instructed by an air traffic service unit (ATSU) to change the type of its callsign temporarily.

2.7.2.5 Aircraft in the heavy wake turbulence category shall include the word 'HEAVY' immediately after the aircraft callsign in the initial call.

2.7.3 Continuation of Communications

2.7.3.1 After initial contact has been firmly established the following words may be omitted provided that no possibility of confusion or ambiguity will result:

(a) the words 'over', 'roger' and 'out' may be omitted;

(b) further identification or callsign may be omitted until termination of the communications.

2.7.3.2 The placement of the callsigns of both the aircraft and the ground radio station *within* an established RTF exchange should be as follows:

Ground to Air: Aircraft callsign – message or reply.

Air to Ground:

(a) Initiation of new information/request etc – Aircraft callsign then message;

(b) Reply – Repeat of pertinent information/readback/ acknowledgement then Aircraft callsign.

G-ABCD descend FL 80	Descending FL 80 G-ABCD
	G-ABCD maintaining FL 80
	G-CD
G-ABCD request descent	G-CD descend to FL 40
	Descending to FL 40 G-CD

2.7.3.3   When it is considered that reception is likely to be difficult, important elements of the message should be spoken twice.

2.7.3.4   When a ground station wishes to broadcast information to all aircraft likely to receive it, the message should be prefaced by the call 'All stations'.

> All stations Wrayton control,
> Colinton VOR on test

No reply is expected to such general calls unless individual stations are subsequently called upon to acknowledge receipt.

2.7.3.5   If there is doubt that a message has been correctly received, a repetition of the message shall be requested either in full or in part.

Phrase	Meaning
Say again	Repeat entire message
Say again ... (item)	Repeat specific item
Say again all before ... (the first word satisfactorily received)	
Say again all after ... (the last word satisfactorily received)	
Say again all between ... and ...	

2.7.3.6 When a station is called but is uncertain of the identification of the calling station, the calling station should be requested to repeat its callsign until identification is established.

> Stourton Ground Fastair 345

Station calling Stourton
Ground say again your call sign

2.7.3.7 When an error is made in a transmission the word 'CORRECTION' shall be spoken, the last correct group or phrase repeated and then the correct version transmitted.

> Fastair 345 Wicken 47
> FL 280 Marlow 07
> correction Marlow 57

Fastair 345 roger

2.7.3.8 If a correction can best be made by repeating the entire message, the operator shall use the phrase 'CORRECTION I SAY AGAIN' before transmitting the message a second time.

2.7.4 **Transfer of communications**

2.7.4.1 An aircraft will normally be advised by the appropriate aeronautical station to change from one radio frequency to another in accordance with agreed procedures.

> Fastair 345 contact
> Wrayton Control 129.1

Wrayton Control 129.1
Fastair 345

In the absence of such advice, the aircraft shall notify the aeronautical station before such a change takes place. Aircraft flying in controlled airspace must obtain permission from the controlling authority before changing frequency.

2.7.4.2 An aircraft may be instructed to 'standby' on a frequency when it is intended that the ATSU will initiate further communications, and to monitor a frequency on which information is being broadcast.

> Fastair 345 standby for
> Kennington weather

Fastair 345

> Fastair 345 monitor 118.9 for
> Tower

Monitor 118.9 for Tower
Fastair 345

2.7.4.3 If the airspace does not dictate that an aircraft must remain in contact with a specific ATSU and the pilot wishes to freecall another agency he should request, or notify such an intention.

> Westbury G-ABCD request
> change to Wrayton
> Information on 125.75

> Wrayton Information
> G-ABCD changing to
> Wrayton Control on 121.5 for
> Practice Pan

2.7.5 Issue of clearance and read back requirements

2.7.5.1 Provisions governing clearances are contained in the PANS-RAC (ICAO Doc 4444). A clearance may vary in content from a detailed description of the route and levels to be flown to a brief standard instrument departure (SID) according to local procedures.

2.7.5.2 Controllers will pass a clearance slowly and clearly since the pilot needs to write it down; wasteful repetition will thus be avoided. Whenever possible a route clearance should be passed to an aircraft before start up and the aircraft's full callsign will always be used. *Generally controllers will avoid passing a clearance to a pilot engaged in complicated taxying manoeuvres and on no occasion when the pilot is engaged in line up or take-off manoeuvres.*

2.7.5.3 An ATC route clearance is *not* an instruction to take-off or enter an active runway. *The words* **'take-off'** *are used only when an aircraft is cleared for take-off. At all other times the word* **'departure'** *is used.*

2.7.5.4 The stringency of the read back requirement is directly related to the possible seriousness of a misunderstanding in the transmission and receipt of ATC clearance and instructions. *ATC route clearances shall always be read back unless otherwise authorised by the appropriate ATS authority* in which case they shall be acknowledged in a positive manner. Read backs shall always include the aircraft callsign.

Fastair 345 cleared from Stourton to Kennington via A1, at FL 60, request level change en-route, squawk 5501	Cleared from Stourton to Kennington via A1, at FL 60, request level change en-route, squawk 5501 Fastair 345
	Fastair 345 correct
Fastair 345 cleared from Stourton to Kennington via A1, Wicken 3 Delta departure, squawk 5501	Cleared from Stourton to Kennington via A1, Wicken 3 Delta departure, squawk 5501, Fastair 345
	Fastair 345 correct
G-ABCD after departure cleared to zone boundary via route echo. Climb to altitude 2000 feet QNH 1008, squawk 6522	After departure cleared to zone boundary via route echo. Climb to altitude 2000 feet QNH 1008, squawk 6522 G-ABCD
	G-CD correct

2.7.5.5 The ATC messages listed below are to be read back in full by the pilot. If the controller does not receive a readback the pilot will be asked to do so. Similarly, the pilot is expected to request that instructions are repeated or clarified if any are not fully understood.

> Level Instructions
>
> Heading Instructions
>
> Speed Instructions
>
> Airways or Route Clearances
>
> Runway in Use
>
> Clearance to Enter, Land On, Take-Off On, Backtrack, Cross, or Hold Short of an Active Runway

SSR Operating Instructions

Altimeter Settings

VDF Information

Frequency Changes

Type of Radar Service

G-ABCD cleared to cross A1 at Wicken, maintain FL 70 whilst in controlled airspace. Report entering the airway	Cleared to cross A1 at Wicken , maintain FL 70 in controlled airspace, wilco. G-ABCD
G-CD hold position	Holding G-CD
G-CD contact Ground 118.05	Ground on 118.05 G-CD
Fastair 345 Squawk 6402	6402 Fastair 345

2.7.5.6 If an aircraft read back of a clearance or instruction is incorrect, the controller shall transmit the word 'NEGATIVE' followed by the correct version.

G-CD QNH 1003	QNH 1013 G-CD
	G-CD Negative, QNH 1003
	QNH 1003 G-CD

2.7.5.7 If at any time a pilot receives a clearance or instruction with which he cannot comply, he should advise the controller using the phrase 'UNABLE' (COMPLY) and give the reason(s).

Fastair 345 Wrayton climb FL 280, cross Wicken FL 150 or above	Wrayton Fastair 345 unable cross Wicken FL 150 due weight

2.7.6   Failure to establish or maintain communication

2.7.6.1   *Air to Ground*

(a)   Check the following points:

   (i)   The correct frequency has been selected for the route being flown.

   (ii)   The Aeronautical Station being called is open for watch.

   (iii) The aircraft is not out of radio range.

   (iv)   Receiver volume correctly set.

(b)   If the previous points are in order it may be that the aircraft equipment is not functioning correctly. Complete the checks of headset and radio installation appropriate to the aircraft.

(c)   If the pilot is still unable to establish communication on any designated aeronautical station frequency, or with any other aircraft, the pilot is to transmit his message twice on the designated frequency preceded by the phrase 'TRANSMITTING BLIND' in case the transmitter is still functioning.

(d)   Where a transmitter failure is suspected, check or change the microphone. Listen out on the designated frequency for instructions. It should be possible to answer questions by use of the carrier wave if the microphone is not functioning (see Chapter 9 para 9.6).

(e)   In the case of a receiver failure transmit reports twice at the scheduled times or positions on the designated frequency preceded by the phrase 'TRANSMITTING BLIND DUE TO RECEIVER FAILURE'.

(f)   An aircraft which is being provided with air traffic control, advisory service or aerodrome flight information is to transmit information regarding the intention of the pilot in command with respect to the continuation of the flight. Specific procedures for the action to be taken by pilots of IFR and Special VFR flights are contained in the appropriate AIP (RAC) sections.

2.7.6.2 *Ground to Air*

After completing checks of ground equipment (most airports have standby and emergency communications equipment) the ground station will request other aeronautical stations and aircraft to attempt to communicate with the aircraft which has failed to maintain contact.

If still unable to establish communication the aeronautical station will transmit messages addressed to the aircraft by blind transmission on the frequency on which the aircraft is believed to be listening.

These will consist of:

(a) The level, route and EAT (or ETA) to which it is assumed the aircraft is adhering.

(b) The weather conditions at the destination aerodrome and suitable alternate and, if practicable, the weather conditions in an area or areas suitable for descent through cloud procedure to be effected. (See AIP RAC Section.)

2.7.7 **Test procedures**

2.7.7.1 Test transmissions should take the following form:

(a) the identification of the aeronautical station being called;

(b) the aircraft identification;

(c) the words 'RADIO CHECK';

(d) the frequency being used.

2.7.7.2 Replies to test transmissions should be as follows:

(a) the identification of the station calling;

(b) the identification of the station replying;

(c) information regarding the readability of the transmission.

2.7.7.3 The readability of a transmission should be classified by the number in the table below, together with any other information regarding the transmission which may be useful to the station making the test.

Scale	Meaning
1	Unreadable
2	Readable now and then
3	Readable but with difficulty
4	Readable
5	Perfectly readable

Borton Tower
G-ABCD radio check 118.7

G-ABCD Borton Tower
readability 5

or

G-CD Borton Tower
readability 3 with a loud
background whistle

or

Station calling Borton Tower
readability 1

2.7.7.4 When it is necessary for a ground station to make test signals, either for the adjustment of a transmitter before making a call or for the adjustment of a receiver, such signals shall not continue for more than 10 seconds. The test should comprise spoken numbers (WUN, TOO, TREE etc) followed by the radio callsign of the station transmitting the test signals.

2.8 PILOTS COMPLAINTS CONCERNING AERONAUTICAL TELECOMMUNICATIONS

Pilots' reports of faults concerning services and facilities in the Aeronautical Mobile, Broadcast and Navigation Services may be recorded on the CAA Form CA 647. The Pilot should ensure that the Briefing Officer, Senior Telecommunications Officer or Senior Controller at the destination or airport of first landing receives full details in order that remedial action can be taken. Reports of local unserviceabilities will be forwarded to the Telecommunications staff if received on RTF by the ATSU.

2.9 AIR TRAFFIC SERVICE COMPLAINTS ABOUT AIRCRAFT COMMUNICATIONS

Aircraft radio faults including technical failure, incorrect operating procedures and misuse of specific radio channels may result in the aircraft operator receiving a communication from the CAA detailing the fault condition inviting the operator to explain and/or state what corrective action has been taken.

CHAPTER 3 – GENERAL PHRASEOLOGY

3.1 INTRODUCTION

3.1.1 The phraseology detailed in this manual has been established for the purpose of ensuring uniformity in RTF communications. Obviously, it is not practicable to detail phraseology examples suitable for every situation which may occur. However, if standard phrases are adhered to when composing a message, any possible ambiguity will be reduced to a minimum.

3.1.2 Some abbreviations, which by their common usage have become part of aviation terminology, may be spoken using their constituent letters rather than the spelling alphabet, for example, ILS, QNH, RVR, etc, (see para 1.2).

3.1.3 The following words may be omitted from transmissions provided that no confusion or ambiguity will result:

(a) 'Surface' and 'knots' in relation to surface wind direction and speed.

(b) 'Degrees' in relation to surface wind direction and headings.

(c) 'Visibility', 'cloud' and 'height' in meteorological reports.

(d) 'Millibars' when giving pressure settings of 1000 mbs and above.

3.1.4 The excessive use of courtesies should be avoided.

3.2 LEVEL INSTRUCTIONS

3.2.1 Only basic level instructions are detailed in this chapter. More comprehensive phrases are contained in subsequent chapters in the context in which they are most commonly used.

3.2.2 The precise phraseology used in the transmission and acknowledgement of climb and descent clearances will vary, depending upon the circumstances, traffic density and nature of the flight operations.

3.2.3   However, care must be taken to ensure that misunderstandings are not generated as a consequence of the phraseology employed during these phases of flight. For example, levels may be reported as altitude, height or flight levels according to the phase of flight and the altimeter setting. Therefore, when passing level messages, the following conventions apply:

(a)   The word 'to' may be omitted from messages relating to FLIGHT LEVELS.

(b)   All messages relating to an aircrafts' *climb or descent* to a HEIGHT or ALTITUDE employ the word 'to' followed immediately by the word HEIGHT or ALTITUDE. Furthermore, the initial message in any such RTF exchange will also include the appropriate QFE or QNH.

(c)   The phrase 're-cleared' should not be employed.

G-CD report your level	G-CD maintaining FL 65
	G-CD descend FL 45
	Descending FL 45 G-CD
G-CD report your level	G-CD maintaining altitude 2500 feet regional QNH 1006
	G-CD descend to altitude 2000 feet Borton QNH 1008
	Descending to altitude 2000 feet Borton QNH 1008 G-CD
	G-CD descend to altitude 1500 feet
	Desending to altitude 1500 feet G-CD

G-CD descend to height
1000 feet QFE 1005

Descending to height
1000 feet QFE 1005 G-CD

3.2.3.1   In the following examples the operations of climbing and descending are interchangeable and examples of only one form are given.

G-CD report passing FL 80

Report passing FL 80 G-CD

G-CD passing FL 80

G-CD maintain 2500 feet

Maintaining 2500 feet G-CD

G-CD climb FL 70

Climbing FL 70 G-CD

G-CD request descent

G-CD descend FL 60

Descending FL 60 G-CD

Fastair 345 after passing
North Cross descend to FL 80

After passing North Cross
descend FL 80 Fastair 345

Fastair 345 stop descent
FL 210

Stop descent FL 210
Fastair 345

3.2.3.2   Occasionally, a higher than normal rate of climb or descent may be required.

| Fastair 345 expedite descent to FL 180 | Expediting descent to FL 180 Fastair 345 |

| Fastair 345 climb FL 280 expedite until passing FL 180 | Climbing FL 280 expediting until passing FL 180 Fastair 345 |

or

Fastair 345 unable expedite climb due weight

3.2.3.3 Under exceptional circumstances, if instant descent/climb is required, the word 'immediately' shall be used.

| Fastair 345 descend immediately to FL 200 due traffic | Descending immediately to FL 200 Fastair 345 |

3.2.3.4 Pilots are expected to comply with ATC instructions as soon as they are issued. However, when a climb/descent is left to the discretion of the pilot, the words 'when ready' shall be used. In these circumstances the pilot will report 'leaving' his present level.

| Fastair 345 when ready climb FL 280 | When ready climb FL 280 Fastair 345 |

Fastair 345 leaving FL 200 climbing FL 280

Fastair 345

3.3   POSITION REPORTING

3.3.1   Position reports shall contain the following elements of information:

(a)   Aircraft identification
(b)   Position
(c)   Time

(d) Level
(e) Next position and ETA

> Fastair 345 Wicken 47
> FL 280 Marlow 57

> Fastair 345

3.3.2 Where adequate flight progress data is available from other sources, such as ground radar, aircraft may be exempted from the requirement to make compulsory position reports.

> Fastair 345 next report at Colinton

> Wilco Fastair 345

> Fastair 345 omit position reports this frequency

> Wilco Fastair 345

> Fastair 345 resume position reporting

> Wilco Fastair 345

3.4   FLIGHT PLANS

3.4.1 A pilot may file a flight plan with an ATSU during flight, although the use of busy RTF channels should be avoided; normally the FIR frequency should be used.

> Wrayton Control G-ABCD I wish to file an airborne flight plan

> G-ABCD Wrayton Control pass your message

3.4.2 The format for an airborne flight plan is as follows:

(a) Aircraft identification and type.
(b) Position and heading.
(c) Level and flight conditions.
(d) Departure aerodrome.
(e) Estimated time at entry point.
(f) Route and point of first intended landing.
(g) True airspeed.
(h) Desired level on airway or advisory route.

3.4.3   During a flight a pilot may elect to cancel an IFR flight plan.

> Wrayton Control G-CD
> cancel my IFR flight plan

> G-CD roger IFR flight plan
> cancelled at time 47

3.4.4   When a pilot has expressed his intention to cancel an IFR flight plan, the ATSU will pass the pilot any available meteorological information which makes it likely that flight in VMC cannot be maintained.

> G-CD IMC reported in the
> vicinity of Kennington

> G-CD roger maintaining IFR

3.5   REPLY TO 'PASS YOUR MESSAGE'

3.5.1   The service that an aircraft requires should be passed in the initial call to the ATSU; when requested by the ATSU to 'pass your message' a suitable reply could contain the following information which, whenever possible, should be given in the following order:

(a)   Aircraft identification and type.
(b)   Estimated position.
(c)   Heading.
(d)   Level.
(e)   Intention (next reporting/turning point/destination)
(f)   Type of service required.

> Westbury Approach, G-ABCD
> request Lower Airspace
> Radar Service

> G-ABCD Westbury Approach
> pass your message

> G-ABCD, T67, 15 miles
> south-east of Westbury,
> heading 350, altitude
> 2500 feet regional QNH 1008,
> destination Walden, request
> Radar Information Service

CHAPTER 4 – AERODROME AIR TRAFFIC SERVICES: AIRCRAFT

4.1 INTRODUCTION

4.1.1 Concise and unambiguous phraseology used at the correct time is vital to the smooth, safe and expeditious running of an aerodrome and associated ATZ. It is not only the means by which instructions and information are passed but it also assists pilots in maintaining an awareness of other traffic in their vicinity, particularly in poor visibility conditions.

4.1.2 Messages will not be transmitted to an aircraft during take-off, the last part of final approach or the landing roll, unless it is necessary for safety reasons, because it will be distracting to the pilot at a time when the cockpit workload is often at its highest.

4.1.3 Local procedures vary from aerodrome to aerodrome and it is impossible to give examples to cover every situation which may arise at the multiplicity of different types of aerodrome. Information in addition to that shown in the examples, eg time checks, etc may be provided as necessary.

4.2 TYPE OF SERVICE

4.2.1 As described in Chapter 2 the type of service provided at an aerodrome falls into one of three categories. In this chapter the examples are confined to those used by air traffic controllers and aerodrome flight information service officers.

4.2.2 Whilst the RTF procedures used by air traffic controllers form the main content of this publication it should be noted that the phraseology used by AFISOs is different from that used by controllers. The Aerodrome Flight Information Service (AFIS) is a service provided at an aerodrome to give information useful for the safe and efficient conduct of flights in the Aerodrome Traffic Zone. From the information received pilots will be able to decide the appropriate course of action to be taken to ensure the safety of flight.

4.2.3 AFIS is available at aerodromes during the hours of operation indicated in the UK AIP. The service is easily identifiable by the callsign suffix 'INFORMATION'.

4.2.4   The Aerodrome Flight Information Service Officer (AFISO) is responsible for:

(a)   Issuing information to aircraft flying in the Aerodrome Traffic Zone to assist pilots in preventing collisions;

(b)   issuing information and instructions, on behalf of the aerodrome operator, to aircraft on the manoeuvring area in order to prevent collisions between aircraft and vehicles/ obstacles on the manoeuvring area, or between aircraft moving on the apron;

(c)   informing aircraft of essential aerodrome information (ie the state of the aerodrome and its facilities);

(d)   alerting the safety services;

(e)   initiating overdue action.

4.2.5   AFISOs are also permitted to pass messages on behalf of other agencies. If they do so, they will include the name of the agency so that pilots will be aware that the message comes from a legitimate source, eg 'Wrayton control clears you to join ...'.

4.3   DEPARTURE INFORMATION AND ENGINE STARTING PROCEDURES

4.3.1   Where no ATIS is provided the pilot may ask for current aerodrome information before requesting start up.

Stourton Ground Fastair 345, request departure information	Fastair 345 Stourton Ground departure runway 32 wind 290 4, QNH 1008, temperature –2, dewpoint –3, RVR 550 metres
	Runway 32, QNH 1008, will call for start up Fastair 345

4.3.2   Requests to start engines are normally made to facilitate ATC planning and to avoid excessive fuel wastage by aircraft delayed on the ground. At certain aerodromes, along with the request, the pilot will state the location of the aircraft and acknowledge receipt of the ATIS broadcast identifying letter.

Stourton Ground Fastair 345, stand 24 information bravo, request start up	Fastair 345 Stourton Ground start up at time 35

4.3.3   When there will be a delay to the departure of the aircraft the controller will normally indicate a time to start up or expect to start up.

Stourton Ground Fastair 345 request start up	Fastair 345 Stourton Ground start up approved, temperature –2

or

Fastair 345 Stourton Ground expect start up at time 35

or

Fastair 345 Stourton Ground expect departure at time 49 start up when ready, temperature –2

4.4   PUSHBACK

4.4.1   At many aerodromes at which large aircraft operate, the aircraft are parked nose-in to the terminal in order to save parking space. Aircraft have to be pushed backwards by tugs before they can taxi for departure. Requests for pushback are made to ATC depending on the local procedures.

Fastair 345 stand 27 request pushback	Fastair 345 pushback approved

or

Fastair 345 negative. Expect one minute delay due B747 taxying behind

4.5 TAXI INSTRUCTIONS

4.5.1 Taxi instructions issued by a controller will always contain a clearance limit, which is the point at which the aircraft must stop unless further permission to proceed is given. For departing aircraft the clearance limit will normally be the holding point of the runway in use, but it may be any other position on the aerodrome depending on the prevailing traffic.

Borton Tower G-ABCD T67 by the south side hangars request taxi for VFR flight to Walden

G-CD taxi to holding point runway 24 via taxiway charlie QNH 1010

Taxi to holding point runway 24 via taxiway Charlie QNH 1010 G-CD

G-CD request surface wind

G-CD surface wind 220 6

G-CD request runway 14

G-CD taxi to holding point runway 14, follow the Seneca coming from your left

Taxi to holding point runway 14. Following the Seneca G-CD

Borton Tower G-ABCD T67 at the fuel station VFR to Walden request taxi

G-CD runway 06 QNH 1008 taxi to holding point runway 14 via taxiway alpha

QNH 1008 G-CD request
taxiway bravo, and backtrack
runway 24

G-CD taxi holding point
runway 24 via taxiway Bravo

Taxi holding point runway 24
via taxiway Bravo G-CD

Borton Tower G-ABCD at the
fuel station request taxi to
flying club

G-CD taxi to holding point
runway 24 via charlie

Taxi holding point runway 24
via charlie G-CD

G-CD holding point
runway 24 request cross

G-CD negative. I will call you

Holding G-CD

G-CD taxi to the flying club,
cross runway 24 at the
threshold report vacated

Taxi to the flying club cross
runway 24 at the threshold
will report vacated G-CD

G-CD runway vacated

G-CD

Note: Report vacated may be omitted when aerodrome control has continuous sight of the aircraft crossing.

4.5.2   Where an ATIS broadcast is established the controller does not need to pass departure information to the pilot when giving taxi instructions.

Fastair 345 information bravo request taxi

Fastair 345 after the B747 passing left to right taxi to holding point runway 28

After B747 taxi to holding point runway 28 Fastair 345

4.6   PRE-DEPARTURE MANOEUVRING

4.6.1   Meticulous care has been taken to ensure that the phraseology which is to be employed during the pre-departure manoeuvres cannot be interpreted as a take-off clearance. This is to avoid the serious consequences that could result if there is any misunderstanding in the granting or acknowledgement of take-off clearances.

4.6.2   At busy aerodromes with a separate ground and tower function, aircraft are usually transferred to the tower frequency at or approaching the holding point.

Fastair 345 contact Tower 118.9

Tower 118.9 Fastair 345

4.6.3 Many types of aircraft carry out engine checks prior to departure and are not always ready for take-off when they reach the holding point.

G-CD report when ready for departure	Wilco G-CD
G-CD ready for departure	G-CD line up
	Lining up G-CD

4.7 TAKE-OFF PROCEDURES

4.7.1 Except in cases of emergency, messages will not be transmitted to an aircraft in the process of taking off or in the final stages of an approach and landing.

Controllers will use the following phraseology for take off.

G-CD cleared take-off	Cleared take-off G-CD

Note: The surface wind will be passed if there is a significant difference to that already passed.

AFISOs will use different phraseology to indicate that there is nothing to prevent an aircraft taking off:

Buckby Information G-BJRD ready for departure	G-RD Buckby Information take-off at your discretion .. surface wind 280 ..... (traffic information)

4.7.2 For traffic reasons a controller may consider it necessary for an aircraft to take off without any delay. Therefore, when given the instruction 'cleared for immediate take-off', the pilot is expected to act as follows:

(a) At the holding point: taxi immediately on to the runway and commence take-off without stopping the aircraft.

41

(b)   If already lined up on the runway: take-off without delay.

Fastair 345 cleared immediate take-off	Cleared immediate take-off Fastair 345

4.7.3   For reason of expedition a controller may wish to line-up an aircraft for departure before conditions allow take-off.

Fastair 345 line-up and wait – vehicle crossing upwind end of runway	
	Line-up and wait Fastair 345
Fastair 345 cleared take-off	Cleared take-off Fastair 345

4.7.4   In poor visibility the controller may state the runway and request the pilot to report when airborne.

Fastair cleared take-off runway 28 report airborne	Cleared take-off runway 28. Wilco. Fastair 345
	Fastair 345 airborne
	Fastair 345 contact Radar 121.75
	Radar 121.75 Fastair 345

4.7.5   Conditional phrases will not be used for movements affecting the active runway(s), except when the aircraft or vehicles concerned are seen by the controller and pilot. When the conditional clearance involves a departing aircraft and an arriving aircraft it is important to ensure that the departing aircraft has correctly identified the arriving aircraft on which the conditional clearance is based. Reference to the arriving aircraft type may be insufficient and a controller may give further information to ensure correct identification. A conditional instruction shall be given as follows:

(a) callsign;

(b) the condition;

(c) the instruction.

Fastair 345 after the landing DC9, line up	After the landing DC9 line up Fastair 345

4.7.6   When several runways are in use and/or there is any possibility that the pilot may be confused as to which one to use, the runway number will be stated.

Fastair 345 cleared take-off runway 09 left	Cleared take-off runway 09 left Fastair 345

4.7.7   Local departure instructions may be given with the take-off clearance. Such instructions are normally given to ensure separation between aircraft operating in the vicinity of the aerodrome.

Fastair 345 after departure climb straight ahead to altitude 2500 feet before turning right. Cleared take-off	After departure climb straight ahead to altitude 2500 feet before turning right. Cleared take-off Fastair 345

G-CD after departure request right turn	G-CD right turn approved cleared take-off
	Right turn approved cleared take-off G-CD

4.7.8   Due to unexpected traffic developments or a departing aircraft taking longer to take-off than anticipated, it is occasionally necessary to rescind the take-off clearance or quickly free the runway for landing traffic.

Fastair 345 take-off immediately or vacate runway	
	Taking-off Fastair 345
Fastair 345 take-off immediately or hold short of runway	
	Holding short Fastair 345

4.7.9 When an aircraft is about to take-off or has commenced the take-off roll, and it is necessary that the aircraft should abandon take-off, the aircraft will be instructed to cancel take-off or stop immediately; these instructions will be repeated.

G-CD hold position, cancel I say again cancel take-off, acknowledge	
	Holding G-CD
Fastair 345 stop immediately I say again Fastair 345 stop immediately, acknowledge	
	Stopping Fastair 345

4.7.10 When a pilot abandons take-off he should, as soon as practicable, inform the tower that he is doing so. Likewise, as soon as practicable, he should inform the tower of the reasons for abandoning take-off if applicable, and request further manoeuvring instructions.

Fastair 345 stopping	Fastair 345
	Fastair 345 request backtrack for another departure
	Fastair 345 backtrack approved

4.8 AERODROME TRAFFIC CIRCUIT

4.8.1

Typical Left-hand Circuit

Position 1 Aircraft reports on downwind leg when abeam upwind end of runway.

Position 2 Base leg report (if required).

Position 3 'Final' report. Clearance to land issued here.

Position 4 'Long final' report (between 8 and 4 miles) when aircraft is on a straight in approach.

Note: For light aircraft operations, circuit dimensions may be reduced but the relative RTF reporting points are maintained.

Figure 1 Critical positions in the traffic circuit

4.8.2 Requests for circuit-joining instructions should be made in sufficient time for a planned entry into the circuit taking other traffic into account. Where ATIS is established, receipt of the broadcast should be acknowledged in the initial call to an aerodrome. When the traffic circuit is a right-hand pattern it shall be specified. A left-hand pattern *need not* be specified although it is *essential* to do so when the circuit direction is variable.

Walden Tower G-ABCD T67 10 miles south altitude 2500 feet regional QNH 1008 request joining instructions	G-CD join righthand downwind runway 27 height 1000 feet QFE 1006
	Join righthand downwind runway 27 height 1000 feet QFE 1006 G-CD

4.8.3　Depending on prevailing traffic conditions and the direction from which an aircraft is arriving, it may be possible to make a straight-in approach.

Walden Tower G-ABCD T67 10 miles south altitude 2500 feet regional QNH 1008 request straight-in approach runway 34	G-CD cleared straight in approach runway 34 surface wind 260 degrees 5 knots QFE 1006 report final
	Cleared straight in approach runway 34 QFE 1006. Wilco. G-CD

4.8.4　The pilot having joined the traffic circuit makes routine reports as required by local procedures.

G-CD downwind	G-CD number 2 follow the Cherokee on base
	Number 2, traffic in sight G-CD
G-CD base	G-CD
G-CD final	G-CD cleared to land runway 34 surface wind 270 7
	Cleared to land runway 34 G-CD

4.8.5   It may be necessary in order to co-ordinate traffic in the circuit to issue delaying or expediting instructions.

G-CD extend downwind number 2 to a Cherokee 4 miles final

Extend downwind, number 2 G-CD

G-CD delaying action. Orbit right report again on base

Orbit right, wilco G-CD

4.8.6   In order to save taxying time when flying training in the traffic circuit pilots may request to carry out a 'touch and go', ie the aircraft lands, continues rolling and takes-off, without stopping.

G-CD downwind request touch and go

G-CD roger

G-CD final

G-CD cleared touch and go runway 34 surface wind calm

Cleared touch and go runway 34 G-CD

or

G-CD unable to approve due traffic make full stop landing cleared to land runway 34 surface wind calm

Cleared to land runway 34 G-CD

4.8.7 It is helpful for traffic management purposes if a controller is informed when an aircraft which has been engaged in multiple approaches is on his last circuit.

G-CD downwind last landing	G-CD roger

4.9 FINAL APPROACH AND LANDING

4.9.1 A 'final' report is made when an aircraft turns onto final approach. If the turn on is made at a distance greater than 4 nm from touchdown a 'long final' report is made. The landing/touch and go/low approach clearance will include the runway designation.

G-CD final	G-CD cleared to land runway 34 surface wind 270 7
	Cleared to land runway 34 G-CD
Fastair 345 long final	Fastair 345 report final surface wind 260 18
	Wilco Fastair 345
	Fastair 345 final
	Fastair 345 cleared to land runway 28 surface wind 270 20
	Cleared to land runway 28 Fastair 345

Note: Where established an 'outer marker' instead of a 'final' report may be made.

4.9.2 The runway may be obstructed when the aircraft makes its 'final' report at 4 nm or less from touchdown but is expected to be clear in good time for the aircraft to make a safe landing. On these occasions the controller will delay landing clearance.

> G-CD final

> G-CD Continue approach surface wind 270 5

> Continue approach G-CD

The controller may or may not explain why the landing clearance has been delayed but the instruction to 'continue' IS NOT an invitation to land and the pilot must wait for landing clearance or initiate a missed approach (see para 4.10.3).

4.9.3 A landing aircraft may be permitted to touch down before a preceding landing aircraft which has landed is clear of the runway provided that:

(a) the runway is long enough to allow safe separation between the two aircraft and there is no evidence to indicate that braking may be adversely affected;

(b) it is during daylight hours;

(c) the controller is satisfied that the landing aircraft will be able to see the preceding aircraft which has landed, clearly and continuously, until it is clear of the runway; and

(d) the pilot of the following aircraft is warned. (Responsibility for ensuring adequate separation rests with the pilot of the following aircraft.)

> Fastair 345, land after the B737 surface wind calm

> Land after the B737 Fastair 345

4.9.4   A pilot may request to fly past the control tower or other observation
         point for the purpose of visual inspection from the ground.

> Fastair 345 request low pass
> unsafe left gear indication

> Fastair 345 cleared low pass
> runway 28 surface wind
> 270 10 not below 500 feet
> QFE 1006 report final

> Cleared low pass runway 28
> not below 500 feet QFE 1006
> wilco Fastair 345

4.9.5   If the low pass is made for the purpose of observing the undercarriage,
         one of the following replies could be used to describe its condition but
         these examples are not exhaustive:

(a)   landing gear appears down;

(b)   right (or left, or nose) wheel appears up (or down);

(c)   wheels appear up;

(d)   right (or left, or nose) wheel does not appear up (or down).

4.9.6   For training purposes, a pilot may request permission to make an
         approach along, or parallel to the runway, without landing.

> Fastair 345 request low
> approach for training

> Fastair 345 cleared low
> approach runway 28 surface
> wind 270 6 not below
> 400 feet report final

> Cleared low approach
> runway 28 not below 400 feet
> wilco Fastair 345

4.9.7   AFISOs will use different phraseology to indicate that there is nothing
         to prevent an aircraft from landing or, alternatively, that the runway is
         obstructed.

> Buckby Information G-BJRD
> final runway 24

> G-BJRD Buckby Information
> land at your discretion
> surface wind 260 6

or

> G-BJRD Buckby Information
> the runway is obstructed

4.10   GO AROUND

4.10.1   Instructions to carry out a missed approach may be given to avert an
         unsafe situation. When a missed approach is initiated cockpit workload
         is inevitably high. Any transmissions to aircraft going around will be
         brief and kept to a minimum.

> Fastair 345 go around
> I say again go around
> acknowledge

> Going around Fastair 345

4.10.2   In the event of a missed approach unless instructions are issued to the
         contrary, an aircraft on an instrument approach is to carry out the
         published missed approach procedure and an aircraft operating VFR is
         to continue into the normal traffic circuit.

4.10.3   In the event of missed approach being initiated by the pilot the phrase
         'going around' shall be used.

> G-CD going around

> G-CD roger

4.11   AFTER LANDING

4.11.1   Unless absolutely necessary, controllers will not give taxi instructions
to pilots until the landing roll is complete. Unless otherwise advised
pilots should remain on tower frequency until the runway is vacated.

Fastair 345 vacate left	Vacate left Fastair 345
Fastair 345 take next right when vacated contact Ground 118.35	Next right when vacated Ground 118.35 Fastair 345
	Kennington Ground Fastair 345 runway vacated
	Fastair 345 Kennington Ground taxi to stand 27 via taxiway alpha
	Stand 27 via taxiway alpha Fastair 345
G-CD taxi to the end report runway vacated	Taxi to the end, wilco G-CD
	G-CD runway vacated
	G-CD taxi to the flying club
	Taxi to the flying club G-CD

4.12 ESSENTIAL AERODROME INFORMATION

4.12.1 Essential aerodrome information is information regarding the manoeuvring area and its associated facilities which is necessary to ensure the safe operation of aircraft. Aerodrome information is passed to aircraft whenever possible prior to start-up or taxi and prior to the commencement of final approach.

Fastair 345 caution
construction work at the
end of Stand 37

... caution work in progress
ahead north side of taxiway
alpha

... caution centre line taxiway
lighting unserviceable

... caution VASIS runway 27
unserviceable

... caution large flock of birds
north of runway 27 near
centre taxiway

CHAPTER 5 – AERODROME AIR TRÁFFIC SERVICES: VEHICLES

5.1 INTRODUCTION

5.1.1 The expeditious movement of vehicles plays an essential supporting role in the operation of an aerodrome. Whenever possible the areas in which vehicles and aircraft operate are segregated. However, there are many occasions when vehicles need to move on the manoeuvring area either for maintenance purposes or in direct support of aircraft operations.

5.1.2 Procedures governing the movement of vehicles vary widely from aerodrome to aerodrome, but certain factors to be taken into account when driving on an aerodrome are common to all:

(a) in general, aircraft are by no means as manoeuvrable as ground vehicles;

(b) the visibility from an aircraft cockpit for ground movement purposes is often restricted compared with a vehicle.

Therefore when vehicles are operating in close proximity to aircraft, drivers should be extremely vigilant and comply with Rule 36/37 of the Rules of the Air 1991 and, if applicable, ATC instructions.

5.1.3 Correct RTF operating technique must be observed by all users. For all vehicles on the movement area, it is important that a continuous listening watch is maintained, not only in case of further instructions or information from the tower, but also so that drivers can be aware of the movements, and intended movements, of other traffic thereby reducing the risk of confliction.

5.2 MOVEMENT INSTRUCTIONS

5.2.1 Drivers on first call should identify themselves by their vehicle call sign, state their position and intended destination (and possibly required route).

> Ground Works 21 stand 27 request proceed to work in progress taxiway hotel

> Works 21 proceed to taxiway hotel via kilo and alpha

> Taxiway hotel via kilo and alpha Works 21

55

5.2.2   If the controller is too busy he will reply 'standby'. This means that the driver should wait until the controller calls back. The driver shall *not* proceed until permission is given.

5.2.3   When there is conflicting traffic the controller may reply 'hold position'. This means that the driver shall not proceed until the controller calls back with permission. All other replies should contain a clearly defined point to which the driver may proceed; this may or may not be the intended destination. If it is not the intended destination drivers must stop at this point and further permission shall be requested.

> Ground Tels 5 exit kilo request proceed to hangar 3

> Tels 5 proceed to hangar 3 via kilo, alpha and foxtrot, cross runway 09. Hold short of runway 14

> Proceeding to hangar 3 via kilo, alpha and foxtrot to cross runway 09 hold short runway 14 Tels 5

5.2.4   Permission to proceed on the apron may include instructions to ensure safe operations.

> Ground Tug 5 gate 21 request proceed to gate 26

> Tug 5 give way to the Fastair BAe 146 on your right, then proceed to gate 26, caution jet blast

> Giving way to the BAe 146 proceeding gate 26, Tug 5

5.3   CROSSING RUNWAYS

5.3.1   Drivers should note carefully the position to which they may proceed, particularly where the intended route involves crossing a runway. Some aerodromes may have procedures that will allow vehicles to proceed to a holding point on the movement area and then request runway crossing instructions. Under no circumstances shall a driver cross a runway unless *positive permission has been given and acknowledged.* A runway vacated report should not be made until the vehicle (and tow) is clear of the designated runway area.

Ground Works 21 by the control tower request proceed to maintenance base	Works 21 proceed to the maintenance area via india and bravo, hold short of runway 27
	Proceed to the maintenance area via india and bravo, hold short of runway 27 Works 21
	Works 21 holding short runway 27
	Works 21 hold position
	Holding Works 21
Works 21 cross runway 27 at threshold report vacated	Cross runway 27 at the threshold Works 21
	Works 21 runway 27 vacated
	Works 21 proceed to maintenance area via North taxiway
	Proceed to maintenance area via North taxiway Works 21

5.3.2   If a vehicle is operating on the runway, it will be instructed to vacate the runway when it is expected that an aircraft will be landing or taking off.

> Works 21 vacate runway 27
> take next right, report
> vacated

> Vacate next right, wilco
> Works 21

> Works 21 runway 27 vacated

> Works 21

5.3.3   When a vehicle is moving on the movement area it may be necessary to inform the vehicle of a potentially dangerous situation and to tell it to stop.

> Works 21 stop immediately
> aircraft crossing ahead

> Stopping Works 21

5.4   VEHICLES TOWING AIRCRAFT

5.4.1   Drivers of vehicles required to tow aircraft should not assume that the receiving station is aware that an aircraft is to be towed. The performance and manoeuvrability of ground vehicles is obviously considerably reduced when towing aircraft and this is taken into account when instructions to such vehicles are issued. Therefore, in order to avoid any confusion, and as an aid to identification, drivers should state the type, and where applicable the operator, of the aircraft to be towed in the first call.

> Ground tug 9 request tow
> Fastair BAe 146 from
> stand 25 to maintenance
> hangar 3

> Tug 9, tow approved from
> stand 25 to maintenance
> hangar 3 via west taxiway

Tow to maintenance hangar 3 via west taxiway Tug 9

Ground tug 9 request tow Fastair BAe 146 from maintenance hangar 3 to stand 25

Tug 9 tow approved from maintenance hangar 3 to stand 25 via holding point foxtrot, hold short runway 32

Tow to stand 25 via foxtrot, hold short runway 32. Tug 9

CHAPTER 6 – GENERAL RADAR PHRASEOLOGY

6.1   INTRODUCTION

6.1.1   This chapter contains general radar phraseology which is commonly used in communications between aircraft and all types of radar unit. Phraseology which is more applicable to approach radar control or area control is to be found in Chapter 7 and 8 as appropriate.

6.1.2   The phrase 'under radar control' shall only be used when a radar control service is being provided. Normally however, the callsign suffix used by the radar unit is sufficient to indicate its function.

6.1.3   In a radar environment heading information given by the pilot and heading instructions given by controllers are normally in degrees magnetic.

6.2   RADAR IDENTIFICATION AND VECTORING

6.2.1   An aircraft must be identified before it can be provided with a radar service. However, the act of identifying aircraft is not a service in itself and pilots should *not* assume that they are receiving a radar service, particularly when they are flying outside controlled airspace.

G-CD report heading	G-CD heading 350
	G-CD for identification turn left heading 320
	Left heading 320 G-CD
	G-CD identified 18 miles north-west of Borton, Radar Advisory
	Radar Advisory G-CD

or

6.2.2   When a controller has identified an aircraft he will inform the pilot,
according to the circumstances, of the following:

(a)   that the aircraft is identified, and

(b)   of the position of the aircraft.

The occasions when the above information will be passed can be
summarised as follows:

Method of Identification	Aircraft flying inside controlled airspaxe		Aircraft flying outside controlled airspace	
	Inform Identified	Pass Position	Inform Identified	Pass Position
SSR	No	No	Yes	Yes
Turn	Yes	Yes	Yes	Yes
Departing aircraft	No	No	Yes	No
Position Report	No	No	Yes	No

6.2.3 The pilot will be warned if identification is lost, or about to be lost, and appropriate instructions given.

> G-CD radar service terminated due radar failure. Resume own navigation. Flight Information available from Wrayton on 125.75

> Changing to Wrayton 125.75 G-CD

> G-CD will shortly be leaving radar cover, radar service terminated. Flight Information available from Wrayton on 125.75

> G-CD changing to Wrayton 125.75

> G-CD

6.3 SECONDARY SURVEILLANCE RADAR

6.3.1 The following phrases are instructions which may be given by controllers to pilots regarding the operation of SSR transponders. The phrases used by controllers are given together with their meanings; assignment of a code *does not* constitute the provision of a radar service.

Phrase	*Meaning*
Squawk (code)	Set the mode and code as instructed
Confirm squawk	Confirm the mode and code set on the transponder
Recycle (mode) (code)	Reselect assignment mode and code

Phrase	Meaning
Squawk Ident	Operate the special position identification feature
Squawk Mayday	Select Emergency
Squawk Standby	Select the standby feature
Squawk Charlie	Select altitude reporting feature
Check altimeter setting and report your level	Check pressure setting and report your level
Stop squawk Charlie	Deselect altitude reporting
Stop squawk Charlie, Wrong indication	Stop altitude report, incorrect level readout
*Verify ... (level)	Check and confirm your level

*Used to verify the accuracy of the Mode C derived level information displayed to the controller.

6.3.2   The pilot must respond to SSR instructions, reading back specific settings.

Fastair 345 squawk 6411	6411 Fastair 345
Fastair 345 confirm squawk	6411 Fastair 345
Fastair 345 recycle 6411	Recycling 6411 Fastair 345
Fastair 345 check altimeter setting	1013 set Fastair 345
Fastair 345 confirm transponder operating	Fastair 345 negative, transponder unserviceable

6.4   RADAR SERVICE

6.4.1   Where it is not self-evident pilots will normally be informed by the controller when they are under radar control, advisory or information service.

Fastair 345 under Radar Control	Radar Control Fastair 345
G-CD Radar Advisory	Radar Advisory G-CD
G-CD Radar Information	Radar Information G-CD
Fastair 345 radar service terminated	Fastair 345

6.5   RADAR VECTORING

6.5.1   Aircraft may be given specific vectors to fly in order to establish separation. Pilots may be informed of the reasons for radar vectoring.

Fastair 345 delaying action. Turn left heading 050	Left heading 050 Fastair 345

6.5.2   It may be necessary for a controller to know the heading of an aircraft as separation can often be established by instructing an aircraft to continue on its existing heading.

Fastair 345 continue present heading	Continue heading Fastair 345
Fastair 345 report heading	Fastair 345 heading 050

> Fastair 345 continue
> heading 050

> Continue heading 050
> Fastair 345

6.5.3 A controller may not know the aircraft's heading but does require the aircraft to fly a particular heading.

> G-CD fly heading 275

> Roger, turning left heading 275, G-CD

> or

> Roger, turning right 20 degrees heading 275, G-CD

6.5.4 When vectoring is complete, pilots will be instructed to resume their own navigation, given position information and appropriate instructions as necessary.

> Fastair 345 resume own navigation direct Wicken magnetic track 070 distance 27 miles

> Wilco Fastair 345

> G-CD resume own navigation position 15 miles southeast Westbury

> Wilco G-CD

6.5.5 Occasionally an aircraft may be instructed to make a complete turn (known as an orbit or a 360 degree turn), for delaying purposes or to achieve a required spacing behind preceding traffic.

> G-CD delaying action, orbit left for sequencing

> Orbit left G-CD

Fastair 345 delaying action. Make a 360 degree turn left	360 turn left Fastair 345

6.6 TRAFFIC INFORMATION AND TRAFFIC AVOIDANCE

6.6.1 Whenever practicable, information regarding traffic on a possible conflicting path should be given in the following form:

(a) relative bearing of the conflicting traffic in terms of the 12 hour clock; or, if the aircraft under service is established in a turn, the relative position of the conflicting traffic in relation to cardinal points ie northwest, south etc;

(b) distance from the conflicting traffic;

(c) direction of flight of the conflicting traffic; and

(d) relative speed of the conflicting traffic or the type of aircraft and level if this is known.

6.6.2 Relative movement should be described by using one of the following terms as applicable:

'closing, converging, parallel, same direction, opposite direction diverging, overtaking, crossing left to right, crossing right to left.'

6.6.3 The controller will inform the pilot when the conflict no longer exists.

G-CD unknown traffic 10 o'clock 6 miles crossing left to right height unknown fast moving. If not sighted turn left heading 270	Left heading 270 G-CD
G-CD clear of traffic resume own navigation direct Walden magnetic track 350 distance 13 miles	Wilco G-CD

6.6.4   Avoiding action to be taken by the pilot is given when the controller
considers that an imminent risk of collision will exist if action is not
taken immediately.

> G-CD avoiding action, turn
> left immediately heading 270
> traffic at 11 o'clock 6 miles
> crossing left to right slightly
> above fast moving

> Left heading 270 G-CD

6.7   RADAR ASSISTANCE TO AIRCRAFT WITH RADIO
COMMUNICATIONS FAILURE

6.7.1   When a controller suspects that an aircraft is able to receive but not
transmit messages, the radar may be used to confirm that the pilot has
received instructions. When further instructions are given they should
be passed slowly, clearly and be repeated.

> G-CD reply not received if
> you read Wrayton turn left
> heading 040 I say again
> turn left heading 040

> G-CD turn observed I will
> continue to pass instructions

or

> Fastair 345 reply not
> received if you read Wrayton
> squawk ident I say again
> squawk ident

> Fastair 345 squawk observed
> I will continue to pass
> instructions

Notes: 1 An aircraft experiencing a radio communications failure is
expected to select the appropriate SSR code.
2 See also Chapter 9.

6.8   DANGER AREA CROSSING SERVICE/DANGER AREA ACTIVITY INFORMATION SERVICE

6.8.1   In-flight information on the status of Danger Areas (DAs) is available from the nominated service units:

(a)   Listed in the UK AIP.

(b)   Detailed on the legend of the appropriate UK 1:500 000 Aeronautical Chart.

6.8.2   When available the DA service will either be a Danger Area Crossing Service (DACS) or a Danger Area Activity Information Service (DAAIS). If there is no reply from the appropriate nominated service unit which is to be called for these services, pilots are advised to assume that the relevant danger area is active.

6.8.3   **Danger Area Crossing Service**

The appropriate nominated service unit will, whenever the DA activity permits, provide a clearance for an aircraft to cross the danger area under a RIS or FIS. The clearance is only in relation to Danger Area activity and does not, in traffic management terms, constitute separation from aircraft which might be operating in the area.

Westbury Approach, G-ABCD request Danger Area Crossing Service of Loudwater Range	G-ABCD Westbury Approach Flight Information Service. Loudwater active. Report 10 miles from Loudwater
	Wilco G-ABCD
	Westbury Approach G-ABCD 10 miles from Loudwater
	G-CD Loudwater remains active. Suggest you re-route

Re-routing to the east of
Loudwater and changing to
Wrayton Information 125.75
G-ABCD

G-ABCD

or

G-ABCD Westbury Approach.
Loudwater not active, range
crossing approved report
vacating the range

Range crossing approved.
Wilco G-ABCD

G-ABCD vacating Loudwater
Range

G-CD Westbury Approach
roger, Flight Information
available from Wrayton on
125.75

Changing to Wrayton on
125.75 G-CD

6.8.4   **Danger Area Activity Information Service**

The nominated service unit will pass to the pilot, on request, an
update on the known activity status of the danger area. Such an update
will assist the pilot to decide whether it would be prudent, on flight
safety grounds, to penetrate the Danger Area. A DAAIS does NOT
constitute a clearance to cross a Danger Area.

Westbury Approach G-ABCD request DAAIS for Loudwater Range	G-ABCD Westbury Approach Loudwater Active/Not Active
	Loudwater Active/Not Active G-ABCD

6.8.5   Full details of DACS/DAAIS can be found in the UK AIP and AICs.

CHAPTER 7 – APPROACH CONTROL

7.1   IFR DEPARTURES

7.1.1   At many airports both arrivals and departures are handled by a single approach control unit. At busier airports departures and arrivals may be handled separately.

7.1.2   In addition to the ATC route clearance, departing IFR flights may be given additional instructions to provide separation in the immediate vicinity.

Fastair 345 Stourton Approach continue heading 040 until passing FL 70 then route direct Wicken

Heading 040 until passing FL 70 then direct Wicken Fastair 345

Fastair 345 report passing FL 70

Fastair 345 passing FL 70 routeing direct Wicken

Fastair 345 contact Wrayton Control 129.1

Wrayton Control 129.1 Fastair 345

7.2   VFR DEPARTURES

7.2.1   Departing VFR flights, when handled by approach control, may be passed information on relevant known traffic in order to assist the pilot in maintaining his own separation. Pilots should report leaving the area of jurisdiction of the approach control units.

> Borton Approach G-CD
> passing the zone boundary

> G-CD Flight Information
> available from Wrayton
> 125.75

> Wrayton Information 125.75
> G-CD

7.2.2   Special VFR flights will be given specific instructions in the clearance to leave the control zone.

> G-CD cleared to the zone
> boundary route via Whiskey
> Special VFR not above
> altitude 1500 feet

> Cleared to the zone
> boundary, route via Whiskey
> Special VFR not above
> altitude 1500 feet G-CD

> G-CD correct

7.3   IFR ARRIVALS

7.3.1   Aircraft flying within controlled airspace will normally receive descent clearance to the clearance limit from the ATCC prior to transfer to an approach control unit. On transfer to approach control further descent instructions may be given.

> Kennington Approach
> Fastair 345 descending FL 90
> Information Charlie

> Fastair 345 Kennington
> Approach cleared direct to
> North Cross descend FL 50

> Direct to North Cross
> descending FL 50 Fastair 345

7.3.2   Arriving IFR flights operating outside controlled airspace are not permitted to enter controlled airspace until cleared to do so. Clearances will be given in a way similar to that in paragraph 7.3.1

above. In the examples below the initial approach fix is Kennington NDB (or VOR), callsign KTN.

Kennington Approach
Fastair 345

Fastair 345 Kennington
Approach pass your message

Fastair 345 25 miles southeast Kennington IFR, FL 125
estimating zone boundary 20
KTN 24 information charlie

Fastair 345 cleared from
10 miles southeast of
Kennington to KTN at FL 60.
Enter controlled airspace at
FL 85 or below

Cleared to KTN at FL 60.
Enter controlled airspace
southeast of Kennington at
FL 85 or below Fastair 345

Fastair 345 expect ILS
approach runway 28 QNH
1011

ILS runway 28 QNH 1011
Request straight in approach
Fastair 345

Fastair 345 cleared straight in
ILS approach runway 28,
descend to altitude 3000 feet
QNH 1011, report
established on the localiser

Cleared straight in ILS
approach runway 28
descending to altitude
3000 feet QNH 1011, wilco
Fastair 345

Fastair 345 established on
the localiser

Fastair 345 QFE 1008

QFE 1008 Fastair 345 runway
in sight

Fastair 345 number 1 contact
Tower 118.7

Number 1 Tower 118.7
Fastair 345

Kennington Tower Fastair 345

Fastair 345 Kennington
Tower report outer marker

Fastair 345

Fastair 345 outer marker

Fastair 345 cleared to land
runway 28 surface wind 280 8

Cleared to land runway 28
Fastair 345

Kennington Approach
G-DCAB

G-DCAB Kennington
Approach pass your message

G-DCAB PA 31 from Stourton
IFR FL 80 estimate KTN 47
information Delta

G-AB remain outside controlled airspace. Time is 41. Expect joining clearance at 44

Remain outside controlled airspace, G-AB

G-AB cleared from 10 miles southeast of Kennington to KTN at FL 80

Cleared from 10 miles southeast of Kennington to KTN at FL 80 G-AB

G-AB expect ILS approach runway 28

G-AB

G-AB descend to altitude 3000 feet QNH 1011

Descending to altitude 3000 feet QNH 1011 G-AB

G-AB cleared ILS approach runway 28 report KTN outbound

Cleared ILS runway 28, wilco G-AB

G-AB KTN outbound

G-AB report procedure turn
complete QFE 1008

Wilco, QFE 1008 G-AB

G-AB procedure turn
complete localiser established

G-AB report at outer marker

Wilco G-AB

G-AB outer marker

G-AB contact Tower 118.9

Tower 118.9 G-AB

Note: *Pilots may be requested to change to tower frequency at any*
point on final approach.

7.3.3   On occasions IFR aircraft do not complete the instrument approach
procedure but request permission to make a visual approach.

G-AB over KTN 3000 feet
field in sight, request visual
approach

G-AB cleared visual approach
runway 28 QFE 1008 contact
Tower 118.7

QFE 1008 Tower 118.7 G-AB

7.3.4   Normally a holding procedure is published. However, the pilot may require a detailed description of a specific holding procedure.

> Fastair 345 hold at
> North Cross FL 60 expect
> onward clearance at time 40

> Hold at North Cross FL 60,
> request holding procedure
> Fastair 345

> Fastair 345 hold at
> North Cross FL 60 inbound
> track 265 degrees turns left
> outbound time 1 minute

It should be noted that the above information is passed in the following order and is for holds *other* than VOR/DME:

(a)   Fix

(b)   Level

(c)   Inbound track

(d)   Right or left turns

(e)   Time of leg

Holding information for VOR/DME substitutes DISTANCE for TIME in (e) above:

> Fastair 345 request holding
> procedure

> Fastair 345 hold on the
> Marlow *VOR/DME* at 20 DME
> FL 100 inbound track
> 265 degrees turns left,
> limiting outbound distance
> 24 DME

7.4   VFR ARRIVALS

7.4.1   Depending on the procedures in use, the pilot of an arriving VFR flight may be required to establish contact with the approach control unit and request instructions before entering its area of jurisdiction eg before entering a control zone. Where there is an ATIS broadcast the pilot should acknowledge that he has received it; where no ATIS broadcast is provided the approach controller will pass the aerodrome data.

Kennington Approach G-DCDN	G-DCDN Kennington Approach pass your message
	G-DCDN C172 from Stourton to Kennington VFR 2500 feet regional QNH 1011 estimating zone boundary 52 Kennington 02 information golf
	G-DN cleared from the zone boundary to Kennington VFR, at 2500 feet Kennington QNH 1012. Traffic information there is a southbound Cherokee 2000 feet VFR estimating zone boundary 53
	Maintain 2500 feet QNH 1012 traffic in sight G-DN
	G-DN report aerodrome in sight
	Wilco G-DN
	G-DN aerodrome in sight
	G-DN contact Tower 118.5
	Tower 118.5 G-DN

Note: *The phraseology for joining the aerodrome traffic circuit is detailed in Chapter 4.*

7.5   SPECIAL VFR FLIGHTS

7.5.1   Special VFR clearances are only issued for flights within Control Zones and are normally at the request of the pilot. The pilot –

(a)   must comply with ATC instructions;

(b)   is responsible for ensuring that his flight conditions enable him to remain clear of cloud, determine his flight path with reference to the surface and to keep clear of obstructions;

(c)   is responsible for ensuring that he flies within the limitations of his licence;

(d)   is responsible for complying with the relevant low flying restrictions of Rule 5 of the Rules of the Air Regulations. Note: Whilst the 1500 ft rule may not apply to a pilot in receipt of a Special VFR clearance, the 'alight clear' rule always applies. The responsibility to determine whether to accept a Special VFR clearance and still comply with this rule rests with the pilot.

(e)   is responsible for avoiding aerodrome traffic zones unless prior permission for penetration has been obtained from the relevant ATSU.

7.5.2   A full flight plan is not required for Special VFR flight but the pilot must give brief details of the callsign, aircraft type and pilot's intentions, including ETA at entry point. A full flight plan is required if the pilot wishes his destination to be notified.

7.5.3   Aircraft are not normally given a specific height to fly but vertical separation from aircraft flying above can be achieved by requiring the Special VFR flight to fly not above a specified level (Section (d) above must be borne in mind by pilots).

7.5.4   No separation will be provided between Special VFR flights which are flying in notified areas or routes where an individual clearance is not required, or between flights using such areas or routes and other flights on Special VFR clearances. Full details of the procedures for Special VFR flights appear in the UK AIP, RAC, Section 1.

7.6   RADAR VECTORS TO FINAL APPROACH

7.6.1   Radar vectors are given to arriving flights to position them onto a pilot-interpreted approach aid, to a point from which a radar-assisted approach can be made or to a point from which a visual approach is made. In the following example an identified aircraft inbound to Kennington is given radar vectors to the ILS. (See fig 2.)

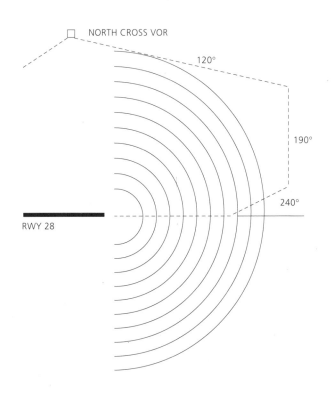

Figure 2 Radar vectors to an ILS approach

Kennington Approach
Fastair 345 FL 60 information
Golf

Fastair 345 Kennington
Approach vectoring for
ILS approach runway 28

Fastair 345

Fastair 345 leave North Cross
heading 120

Leave North Cross heading
120 Fastair 345

Fastair 345 report speed

Fastair 345 speed 260 knots

Fastair 345 reduce speed to
210 knots

210 knots Fastair 345

Fastair 345 leaving North
Cross heading 120

Fastair 345 roger descend to
Altitude 2500 feet QNH 1011
number 4 in traffic

Descending to altitude
2500 feet QNH 1011
Fastair 345

Fastair 345 position 10 miles
northeast of Kennington.
This is a right hand circuit
for runway 28

Fastair 345

Fastair 345 turn right
heading 190 base leg, no ATC
speed restrictions

Right heading 190. No speed
restriction Fastair 345

Fastair 345 12 miles from
touchdown turn right
heading 240 closing localiser
from the right report
localiser established

Right heading 240 ILS wilco
Fastair 345

Fastair 345 localiser
established

Fastair 345 descend on the
ILS QFE 1008

Wilco, QFE 1008 Fastair 345

Fastair 345 contact Tower
118.5

Tower 118.5 Fastair 345

7.6.2   In the example above the approach speed of the aircraft is reduced to
maintain separation between aircraft in an approach sequence. Where

speed adjustment would be insufficient, it may be necessary to issue additional vectors.

Fastair 345 delaying action make a 360 turn to the left	360 turn to the left Fastair 345
Fastair turn left heading 220 for spacing	Left heading 220 Fastair 345

7.7 DIRECTION FINDING

7.7.1 The aeronautical stations that offer a VHF Direction Finding (VDF) service are listed in the UK AIP (COM) section. Some VDF stations stipulate that the service is not available for en-route navigation purposes (except in emergency). VDF bearing information will only be given when conditions are satisfactory and radio bearings fall within calibrated limits of the station. If the provision of a radio bearing is not possible the pilot will be told of the reason.

A pilot may request a bearing or heading using the appropriate phrase or Q code to specify the service required. Each aircraft transmission shall be ended by the aircraft call sign. A VDF station will provide the following as requested:

(1) QDR – Magnetic bearing of the aircraft from the station (ie ..... Approach G-ABCD request QDR G-ABCD).

(2) QDM – Magnetic heading to be steered by the aircraft (assuming no wind) to reach the VDF station (ie ..... Approach G-ABCD request QDM G-ABCD).

(3) QTE – True bearing of the aircraft from the station (ie ..... Approach G-ABCD request True Bearing (or QTE) G-ABCD).

The direction-finding station will reply in the following manner:

(1) the appropriate phrase or Q code

(2) the bearing or heading in degrees in relation to the direction-finding station

(3)   the class of bearing

(4)   the time of observation, if necessary.

<table>
<tr><td>

Kennington Approach
G-DCAB request QDM
G-DCAB

</td><td>

G-DCAB Kennington
Approach QDM 090 degrees
class bravo

</td></tr>
<tr><td></td><td>

QDM 090 degrees class bravo
G-DCAB

</td></tr>
<tr><td>

True bearing, true bearing,
Kennington Approach
G-DCAB request true bearing
G-DCAB

</td><td>

G-DCAB Kennington
Approach true bearing
276 degrees true, I say again,
276 degrees true, class bravo

</td></tr>
<tr><td></td><td>

True bearing 276 degrees
class bravo G-DCAB

</td></tr>
</table>

7.7.2   The accuracy of the observation is classified as follows:

Class A – Accurate within plus or minus 2 degrees

Class B – Accurate within plus or minus 5 degrees

Class C – Accurate within plus or minus 10 degrees

Class D – Accuracy less than Class C

Note: Normally no better than Class B bearing will be available.

7.8   QGH PROCEDURE

7.8.1   QGH letdowns may be provided, when requested by a pilot, at aerodromes where the procedure is approved. The procedure provides for control of an aircraft from its initial approach level to a position from which an approach can be completed visually (see figure 3); this approach may not be aligned with a runway.

7.8.2   On receiving a request for a QGH the aircraft is to be homed overhead the VDF aerial at or descending to the lowest available flight level/

altitude taking into account the minimum safe flight level or safety altitude as appropriate. During homing the following message will be passed to the pilot:

> G-ABCD, Kennington Approach set heading 230, maintain FL 40 (procedure minimum 670 feet (if requested))

> Turning left heading 230 maintaining FL 40 (procedure minimum 670 feet), FL 40, G-ABCD

7.8.3   During the procedure aircraft replies are used to obtain D/F bearings. Pilots may be asked to make additional transmissions for D/F. With some equipment the full callsign is sufficient to obtain bearings.

> G-ABCD transmit for D/F

> G-ABCD transmitting for D/F
> G-ABCD

or

> G-ABCD

Figure 3 QGH procedure

7.8.4 Two D/F indications are required to confirm the aircraft is overhead the VDF aerial; then instructions are given to achieve the desired outbound track.

G-ABCD transmit for overhead

G-ABCD transmitting for D/F
G-ABCD

G-ABCD transmit for overhead

G-ABCD transmitting for D/F
G-ABCD

G-ABCD indicating overhead
turn left heading 105 report
steady

Left heading 105. Wilco.
G-ABCD

G-ABCD steady heading 105

7.8.5 On completion of the overhead turn and when bearings indicate the aircraft is outbound the controller starts timing the outbound leg and provides heading corrections derived from a series of bearings to make good the desired outbound track. Descent instructions and the appropriate pressure setting are also given during this procedure.

G-ABCD set QNH 1011

QNH 1011 G-ABCD

G-ABCD descend to altitude
2500 feet. Report level

Descending to altitude
2500 feet wilco G-ABCD

7.8.6   On completion of the timed outbound leg (eg 3 min) the aircraft is instructed to turn onto a heading to achieve the final approach track.

G-ABCD turn left heading 270, report steady	Left heading 270 wilco G-ABCD

7.8.7   When the aircraft reports steady on completion of the inbound turn, headings will continue to be given to achieve the inbound track. During the inbound leg the controller will pass instructions to be followed in the event of a missed approach (Note: At military airfields the weather and missed approach procedure may be passed at an earlier stage in the procedure). Descent clearance to minimum descent height and the QFE will be given on this leg.

G-ABCD in the event of a missed approach climb straight ahead to altitude 2500 feet, turn right and hold at the KTN	In the event of a missed approach climb straight ahead to altitude 2500 feet, turn right and hold at the KTN, G-ABCD
	G-ABCD set QFE 1008
	QFE 1008 G-ABCD
G-ABCD continue descent to minimum descent height. Report field in sight	Descending to minimum descent height wilco G-ABCD

7.8.8   If the pilot has not reported 'visual' by the time minimum descent height is reached he may be instructed to maintain level flight until he is overhead the VDF.

If the aircraft is not 'visual' when overhead the VDF, the controller will give the instruction to carry out a missed approach procedure.

7.9   VDF PROCEDURE

7.9.1   This is a procedure whereby a pilot requests a series of QDMs to home to a VDF station or or near an aerodrome and to carry out a prescribed VDF instrument approach procedure to the aerodrome. VDF procedures are notified in the RAC section of the UK AIP.

7.9.2   Requests for QDMs are normally initiated by the pilot at intervals of about 1 minute during the initial stages of the homing, increasing in frequency as the VDF overhead is approach. During this procedure QDMs are requested as required to achieve and maintain the specified tracks. *The VDF Procedure is totally pilot interpreted.*

Borton Approach, G-ABCD, information Delta, request homing and VDF approach

G-ABCD, Borton Approach, pass your message

G-ABCD, T67, 15 miles northwest of Borton, heading 130, FL 55, IFR, inbound Borton, request homing and VDF approach, G-ABCD

G-ABCD, cleared to the VDF overhead at altitude 3000 feet Borton QNH 1010, QDM 120 class bravo, report overhead

Cleared to the VDF overhead at altitude 3000 feet Borton QNH 1010, QDM 120 class bravo, Wilco, G-ABCD

7.9.3   The pilot employs a series of QDMs to home to the VDF overhead positioning himself to arrive from a direction which will entail the minimum of manoeuvring in the overhead to proceed outbound on the specified track.

90

G-ABCD request QDM
G-ABCD

G-ABCD QDM 120

QDM 120 G-ABCD

G-ABCD maintaining
3000 feet, request QDM
G-ABCD

G-ABCD roger, QDM 130

QDM 130 G-ABCD

G-ABCD request QDM,
G-ABCD

G-ABCD QDM 145, cleared
VDF approach runway 34

QDM 145, cleared VDF
approach runway 34 G-ABCD

G-ABCD request QDM
G-ABCD

G-ABCD QDM 150

QDM 150 G-ABCD

G-ABCD request QDM
G-ABCD

G-ABCD no bearing

G-ABCD request QDM
G-ABCD

G-ABCD no bearing

G-ABCD overhead turning
outbound G-ABCD

G-ABCD report descending
in the procedure QFE 1007

Wilco, QFE 1007 G-ABCD

7.9.4   The pilot starts timing the outbound leg and, employing a series of
QDMs to establish and maintain the prescribed track, descends as
notified for the procedure. The timed outbound leg ends with a turn
(normally level) onto the final approach QDM.

G-ABCD request QDM
G-ABCD

G-ABCD QDM 340

G-ABCD descending
outbound QDM 340 G-ABCD

G-ABCD roger, report base
turn complete

> Wilco G-ABCD

> G-ABCD request QDM
> G-ABCD

> G-ABCD QDM 350

> QDM 350 G-ABCD

7.9.5   At the end of the outbound leg the pilot turns as prescribed onto the final approach QDM using a series of QDMs during the turn to achieve the final QDM.

> G-ABCD request QDM
> G-ABCD

> G-ABCD QDM 345

> QDM 345 G-ABCD

> G-ABCD request QDM
> G-ABCD

> G-ABCD QDM 342

> QDM 342 G-ABCD

> G-ABCD base turn complete,
> descending inbound,
> G-ABCD

G-ABCD continue approach,
report field in sight
QFE 1007

Wilco, QFE 1007 G-ABCD

G-ABCD QDM 338

QDM 338 G-ABCD

G-ABCD request QDM
G-ABCD

G-ABCD QDM 340

QDM 340 G-ABCD

G-ABCD field in sight

G-ABCD contact Tower 118.7

Tower 118.7 G-ABCD

7.9.6   If no visual contact is gained, a missed approach is initiated at the
missed approach point which is normally the VDF overhead.

G-ABCD request QDM
G-ABCD

G-ABCD no bearing

G-ABCD nothing seen,
initiating missed approach
procedure G-ABCD

7.10 NDB(L) AND VOR PROCEDURES

7.10.1 NDB(L) and VOR instrument approach procedures are pilot
interpreted procedures notified for particular aerodromes and runways
where procedural tracks are defined by NDB(L) bearings or VOR
radials. Some NDB(L) and VOR procedures may include marker
beacons or DME to provide ranging information. Aircraft may also be
radar vectored to an NDB(L) or VOR final approach track. An example
of an NDB(L) instrument approach procedure to an aerodrome outside
controlled airspace follows; similar RTF phraseology may be employed
in VOR procedures.

Borton Approach, G-ABCD
inbound Borton, information
delta

G-ABCD, Borton Approach
pass your message

G-ABCD, T67, 20 miles south
of Borton, FL 80, IFR,
estimating BTN 47, request
beacon approach

G-ABCD cleared to BTN at
FL 80, no delay expected

Cleared to BTN FL 80, no
delay expected G-ABCD

G-CD expect beacon approach runway 34, descend to altitude 3000 feet, Borton QNH 1015, report reaching

Expect beacon approach runway 34, descending to altitude 3000 feet Borton QNH 1015, wilco, G-CD

G-CD maintaining 3000 feet

G-CD roger, cleared for beacon approach runway 34, report beacon outbound

Cleared for beacon approach runway 34, wilco, G-CD

G-CD beacon outbound

G-CD report base turn complete, QFE 1013

Wilco, QFE 1013 G-CD

G-CD base turn complete

G-CD report at 4 DME

Wilco, G-CD

G-CD 4 DME

G-CD roger, contact Tower 118.7

Tower 118.7, G-CD

7.11   SURVEILLANCE RADAR APPROACHES

7.11.1   During a surveillance radar approach (SRA) the pilot is given distances from touchdown, advisory height information and azimuth instructions to enable him to make an approach to a particular runway. Controllers at civil aerodromes in the UK will normally pass advisory heights based on the QFE.

Fastair 345 this will be a surveillance radar approach terminating at half a mile from touchdown. Check your minima, step down fixes and missed approach point

Fastair 345

7.11.2   If a pilot wishes to conduct his approach by reference to altitude he must inform the controller and request the QNH. The controller, when passing the QNH, will add the aerodrome or touchdown elevation to the advisory heights. All references to the level of the aircraft will then be to altitude.

7.11.3   If the pilot reports visual in the early stages of the approach he will be asked whether he wishes to continue the SRA. Normally aircraft will not be transferred to aerodrome control until after they have completed the SRA approach and have landed.

7.11.4   The range at which the descent begins depends on the height of the aircraft during the intermediate phase and the angle of the glide path. The following example commences when the aircraft, having been descended to 2000 feet QFE, is awaiting instructions for an approach on a three degree glide path.

97

Fastair 345 turn right heading 275 final approach	Right heading 275 Fastair 345
Fastair 345 8 miles from touchdown. Your descent will begin at $6^1/_2$ miles. Check wheels	Fastair 345
Fastair 345.7 miles from touchdown. Report runway or approach lights in sight	Fastair 345
Fastair 345 after landing contact Kennington tower on 118.5	After landing Kennington tower 118.5 Fastair 345
Fastair 345 approaching $6^1/_2$ miles from touchdown. Commence descent now to maintain a three degree glide path	Descending Fastair 345
6 miles from touchdown. Height should be 1850 feet	Fastair 345
Slightly left of track. Turn right heading 280	Heading 280 Fastair 345
$5^1/_2$ miles from touchdown. Height should be 1700 feet	Fastair 345
5 miles from touchdown. Height should be 1550 feet. Heading 280 is good	Fastair 345

4½ miles from touchdown.
Height should be 1400 feet.
Slightly right of track. Turn
left 3 degrees heading 277

Heading 277, Fastair 345

4 miles from touchdown.
Height should be 1250 feet.
Do not reply to further
instructions

(the gap between further transmissions will be less than 5 seconds)

3½ miles from touchdown.
Height should be 1100 feet.
Cleared to land runway 28.
Surface wind calm

3 miles from touchdown.
Height should be 950 feet.
Heading 277 is good

2½ miles from touchdown.
Height should be 800 feet.
On track

2 miles from touchdown.
Height should be 650 feet.
Check minimum descent
height

1½ miles from touchdown.
Height should be 500 feet.
On track

1 mile from touchdown.
Height should be 350 feet

On track. Half a mile from
touchdown. Approach
completed. Out

7.11.5 When the SRA terminates at 2 miles from touchdown the advisory level checks at half mile intervals are omitted and pilots are expected to reply to all transmissions from the ground station.

7.11.6 Height checks below the category A aircraft OCH will be omitted.

7.12 MILITARY AERODROME TRAFFIC ZONES AND ASSOCIATED PENETRATION SERVICES

7.12.1 Comprehensive details of MATZ and the associated penetration service, including controlling aerodromes, contact frequencies and hours of watch, are contained in the UK AIP RAC Section, AICs, AIP Supplements or System NOTAM.

7.12.2 While every effort will be made to ensure safe separation, some civil aircraft flying within the MATZ may not be known to controllers and therefore pilots should keep a careful look-out at all times.

7.12.3 Pilots requiring a MATZ penetration service must establish two way RTF communication on the appropriate frequency with the aerodrome controlling the zone when 15 nm or 5 min flying time from the boundary whichever is the sooner. When asked by the controller to 'pass your message' the pilot should pass the following information:

(a)   Callsign
(b)   Type of aircraft
(c)   Position
(d)   Heading
(e)   Altitude/FL
(f)   Intentions (eg destination)

> Westbury Approach this is
> G-ABCD request MATZ
> penetration

> G-ABCD Westbury Approach
> pass your message

> G-ABCD, Slingsby over
> Middleton heading 350,
> altitude 2500 feet regional
> QNH 1005 en-route Walden

> G-CD, cross MATZ at 1500 ft
> on Westbury QNH 1006.
> Report entering and leaving
> the MATZ

> Cross MATZ at 1500 ft on
> Westbury QNH 1009, Wilco
> G-CD

Whilst working a MATZ unit, pilots are expected to comply with any instructions issued by controllers and maintain a listening watch on the allocated RTF frequency. They should not change heading or level without giving prior warning and should advise when leaving the MATZ. At some MATZ units, the Zone controller is responsible for MATZ penetration services.

7.13   LOWER AIRSPACE RADAR SERVICE

7.13.1   The Lower Airspace Radar Service (LARS) is available to assist pilots flying outside regulated airspace up to and including FL 95. LARS is normally provided within 30 nm of the nominated unit and is provided at the discretion of the controller. Therefore, when primary task loadings are high, LARS may not be available. The services available are Radar Advisory Service (RAS) or Radar Information Service (RIS); the type of service required should be specified as detailed at para 7.13.3 below.

7.13.2   Pilots requiring a LARS should establish RTF communication with the appropriate ATSU using the following format:

> Westbury Approach
> G-ABCD request Lower
> Airspace Radar Service
>
> G-ABCD Westbury Approach
> pass your message

7.13.3   Once communications have been estbalished the pilot should pass the following details:

(a)   Callsign and type of aircraft

(b)   Estimated position

(c)   Heading

(d)   Level (or level and band for traffic wishing to carry out general handling)

(e)   Intention (next reporting/turning point, destination etc)

(f)   Type of service required (RAS or RIS)

> G-ABCD, T67, 15 miles SE
> Westbury heading 350
> altitude 2500 feet regional
> QNH 1004, destination
> Walden, request Radar
> Advisory Service

7.13.4   The identification procedure does not imply that a radar service is being provided. The pilot must not assume that he is in receipt of a RAS or RIS until the controller has made a positive statement to that effect based on an 'accord' being reached between the pilot and the controller of the type of service to be provided.

7.13.5   RAS and RIS are defined as follows:

(a)   **Radar Advisory Service.** RAS is an air traffic radar service in which the controller will provide advice necessary to maintain standard separation between participating aircraft and in which he will pass to the pilot the bearing, distance and, if known, level of conflicting non-participating traffic, together with advice on action necessary to resolve the confliction. Where time does not permit this procedure to be adopted, the controller will pass avoiding action to resolve the confliction followed by information on the conflicting traffic. Under a RAS the following conditions apply:

(i)   The service may be requested under any flight rules or meteorological conditions;

(ii)   Controllers will expect the pilot to accept vectors or level allocations which may require flight in IMC. **Pilots not qualified to fly in IMC should accept a RAS only where compliance with ATC advice permits the flight to be continued in VMC;**

(iii)   A pilot who chooses not to comply with advisory avoiding action must inform the controller. The pilot will then become responsible for initiating any avoiding action that may subsequently prove necessary;

(iv)   The pilot must advise the controller before changing heading or level;

(v)   Information on conflicting traffic will be passed until the confliction is resolved;

(vi)   There is no legal requirement for pilots flying outside Aerodrome Traffic Zones or Controlled Airspace to comply with instructions because of the advisory nature of the service. However, pilots will be assumed to be complying with ATC instructions unless they state otherwise. Within a MATZ, ATC instructions to military pilots are mandatory.

(b)   **Radar Information Service (RIS).** RIS is an air traffic radar service in which the controller will only provide traffic information; he will inform the pilot of the bearing, distance and, if known, the level of the conflicting traffic. No avoiding action will be offered. The pilot is wholly responsible for maintaining separation from other aircraft whether or not the controller has passed traffic information. Under a RIS, the following conditions apply:

(i)   The service may be requested under any flight rules or meteorological conditions;

(ii)   The controller will only update details of conflicting traffic after the initial warning at the pilot's request, or if the controller considers that the conflicting traffic continues to constitute a definite hazard;

(iii) The pilot will advise the controller before changing level, level band, or route;

(iv) RIS may be offered by the controller when the provision of RAS is impracticable;

(v) Request for a RIS to be upgraded to a RAS will be actioned as soon as practicable. If a RAS cannot be provided the controller will continue to offer a RIS.

7.13.6 Details of LARS, including participating ATSUs, their hours of operation and contact frequencies, are contained in the UK AIP RAC Section and AICs.

CHAPTER 8 – AREA CONTROL

8.1 AREA CONTROL UNITS

8.1.1 The following examples of phraseology are suitable for use at air traffic control centres according to the requirements of the prevailing traffic situation.

Fastair 345 request descent	Fastair 345 maintain FL 280 expect descent after Marlow
	Maintaining FL 280 Fastair 345
Fastair 345 descend FL 120. Cross Colinton FL 170 or above	Descending FL 120. Cross Colinton FL 170 or above Fastair 345
Fastair 345 are you able to cross Colinton at time 52	Affirm Fastair 345
	Fastair 345 cross Colinton not before time 52
	Cross Colinton not before time 52 Fastair 345

8.2 POSITION INFORMATION

8.2.1 In order to assist in establishing separation, pilots may be instructed to provide additional position report information as well as routine reports.

Fastair 345 report Colinton	Fastair 345

	Fastair 345 Colinton 47 FL 170 descending FL 120, abeam KTN at 55
	Fastair 345
Fastair 345 report 25 miles DME from Kennington	Wilco Fastair 345
Fastair 345 report your DME distance from Kennington	Fastair 345 26 miles
Fastair 345 report crossing radial 270 Kennington VOR	Wilco Fastair 345

8.3   FLIGHTS JOINING AIRWAYS

8.3.1   Aircraft requiring to join an airway should make their request to the appropriate ATSU. Where no flight plan has been filed, the request should include the filing of an airborne flight plan (see Chapter 3). Where a flight plan has already been filed an abbreviated call may be made.

Wrayton Control G-RDVC request clearance to enter controlled airspace northeast of Marlow at FL 240	G-RDVC cleared from 8 miles northeast of Marlow to Colinton via A1, maintain FL 240, squawk 5507
	Cleared from 8 miles northeast of Marlow to Colinton, via A1, maintain FL 240, squawk 5507 G-RVDC
	G-RVDC correct

8.3.2   Because of the prevailing traffic situation, a joining clearance may not be issued immediately.

| G-RVDC remain outside controlled airspace expect joining clearance at time 55 time is 44 | Remaining outside controlled airspace G-RVDC |

8.3.3   In the event that the requested flight level is already occupied the controller will offer an alternative.

| G-RVDC request FL 240 | G-RVDC unable approve FL 240, FL 220 available |
| | G-RVDC accept FL 220 |

8.4   FLIGHTS LEAVING AIRWAYS

8.4.1   Flights leaving controlled airspace will normally be given a specific point at which to leave, together with any other relevant instructions necessary to ensure separation.

| G-RVDC cleared to leave controlled airspace northeast of Marlow maintain FL 220 whilst in controlled airspace | Cleared to leave controlled airspace northeast Marlow maintain FL 220 in controlled airspace G-RVDC |

8.4.2   An aircraft may request permission to leave controlled airspace by descent.

| G-RDVC request permission to leave controlled airspace by descent | G-RDVC cleared to leave controlled airspace by descent. Report passing altitude 5500 feet (Regional) QNH 1014 |
| | Cleared to leave controlled airspace by descent will report passing altitude 5500 feet (Regional) QNH 1014 G-RDVC |

In the above example the base of the airway is 5500 feet.

8.5   FLIGHTS CROSSING AIRWAYS

8.5.1   An aircraft requiring to cross an airway should make its request to the appropriate ATSU.

Wrayton Control G-ABCD request crossing of A1 at Wicken	G-ABCD Wrayton Control pass your message
	G-ABCD T67 20 miles north of Wicken heading 220 FL 80 IMC request crossing clearance of airway A1 at Wicken FL 80 at 1033
	G-ABCD cleared to cross A1 at Wicken, maintain FL 80 whilst in controlled airspace. Report entering the airway
Cleared to cross A1 at Wicken maintain FL 80 in controlled airspace. Wilco. G-ABCD	

8.6   FLIGHTS HOLDING EN-ROUTE

8.6.1   When an aircraft is required to hold en-route, the controller will issue holding instructions and a time at which onward clearance can be expected. Where it is not self-evident, the reason for the delay should also be given.

Fastair 345 hold at Colinton FL 170, expect onward clearance at 03, landing delays at Kennington 20 minutes	Hold at Colinton FL 170 expect onward clearance at time 03 Fastair 345

CHAPTER 9 – EMERGENCY RTF PROCEDURES

9.1 INTRODUCTION

9.1.1 This chapter describes the characteristics of the VHF International Aeronautical Emergency Service and the RTF procedures which should be used under the Aeronautical Mobile Service during an emergency in the UK. Additional information is published in the UK AIP (SAR and COM) sections and AICs.

9.2 VHF EMERGENCY SERVICE

9.2.1 Characteristics of the service

9.2.1.1 The UK has two Distress and Diversion (D&D) Sections located at the London and Scottish Air Traffic Control Centres (LATCC and ScATCC). They are manned by RAF control staff who are assisted in the provision of an emergency service on the International Aeronautical Emergency Frequency 121.50 MHz by suitably equipped civil and military units and certain HM Coastguard stations. The service is available continuously to pilots flying within UK airspace who are in distress, in urgent need of assistance, or experiencing difficulties, (ie temporarily unsure of position) which could lead to a state of emergency. The service may also be available for practices provided that no actual emergency is in progress on the UHF or VHF distress frequencies. More information on the emergency service for civil pilots can be found in the UK AIP (COM 0-6).

9.2.1.2 The primary role of the D&D Sections is to provide military and civil pilots with an emergency aid and position fixer service. In respect of civil aircraft incidents on VHF they rely for position fixing on DF bearing information obtained by telephone from external units equipped with VDF. This fixing procedure takes time and may require several minutes of concentrated activity because it involves the manual plotting onto 1:250,000 charts of the bearings received. (An automated 121.5 MHz autotriangulation position fixing system, which will cover most of central and southeast England, is being procured and is due to be in service by 1993.) The quality of the position fixes is determined by the availability of VDF bearings, and thus, depends largely on the height of an aircraft and its distance from the VDF stations. The coverage of the VHF fixing service is limited below 3000 ft amsl; indeed, the ability to locate aircraft at low altitude by the use of VDF may be severely inhibited (because of the effects of high ground) over much of Scotland, Wales and SW England. In circumstances where 121.5 MHz DF data is lacking, the controller's ability to assist a pilot who is uncertain of his position is very limited, and will depend on such factors as the availability of SSR information and the amount and accuracy of the information provided by the pilot about his route, last known position and observed landmarks.

9.2.1.3 Certain UK aerodromes can also offer civil pilots an effective emergency communications and aid service. Some maintain a continuous watch on 121.50 MHz, but not all are equipped with VDF or SSR. Others do not normally listen out on 121.50 MHz but they do have VDF and may be asked by the Emergency Controller to provide DF bearing information on an aircraft, and other assistance. Where a bearing is required for fixing purposes from an airfield which has VDF but not on 121.5 MHz, the Emergency Controller may instruct the pilot to change temporarily to the frequency on which VDF is available.

9.3   USE OF THE SERVICE – GENERAL PROCEDURES

9.3.1   Pilots should address their emergency calls on 121.50 MHz to 'London Centre' when south of N55°, and 'Scottish Centre' when north of N55°. If doubt exists about the appropriate centre, it is not necessary to address a specific station. Once two-way communication has been established, pilots should not leave 121.5 MHz without telling the controller. The use of special D&D Sections at the ATCCs in the provision of emergency services is unique to the UK. Detailed information on related UK Search and Rescue (SAR) procedures is contained in the SAR Section of the UK AIP.

9.3.2   Pilots are urged – in their own interests – to request assistance from the emergency service as soon as there is any doubt about the safe conduct of their flight. Even then, the provision of assistance may be delayed if a pilot does not pass clear details of his difficulties and requirements. For example, a vague request from a pilot for 'confirmation of position' is unlikely to be accorded as much priority as would be given to a statement that he is lost.

9.3.3   If a pilot is already in communication with a civil or military ATSU, before the emergency arises, assistance should be requested from the controller on the frequency in use. In this case, any SSR code setting previously assigned by ATC (other than the Conspicuity Code 7000) should be retained until instructions are received to change the code setting.

9.3.4   If, however, the pilot is not in direct communication with an ATSU and the aircraft is equipped with an SSR transponder it should be switched, preferably before the emergency call is made, to Mode A Emergency Code 7700, with Mode C if available. If the transponding aircraft is high enough to be within secondary radar cover, the selection of the Emergency 7700 Code will alert the Emergency Controller to the presence of an incident by means of an audio and visual warning. The received SSR plot will show the precise location of the aircraft on the controller's radar display, and will then obviate the need for the emergency controller to carry out the more time-consuming manual aircraft position plotting procedure. Information on SSR operating procedurs, including Special Purpose Codes 7700 (Emergency), 7600 (Radio Failure) and 7500 (Hijack or Other Act of Violence) are detailed in the RAC Section of the UK AIP.

9.4   STATES OF EMERGENCY

9.4.1   The states of emergency are classified as follows:

(1)   *Distress*   The aircraft is threatened by serious or imminent danger and is in need of immediate assistance.

(2)   *Urgency*   The calling station has a very urgent message to transmit concerning the safety of an aircraft, or of some person on board or within sight.

9.5   EMERGENCY MESSAGE

9.5.1   The emergency message should contain the following information (time and circumstance permitting) and, whenever possible, should be passed in the order given:

(a) 'MAYDAY/MAYDAY/MAYDAY' (or 'PAN PAN/PAN PAN/PAN PAN');

(b) Name of the station addressed (when appropriate and time and circumstances permitting);

(c) Callsign;

(d) Type of aircraft;

(e) Nature of the emergency;

(f) Intention of the person-in-command;

(g) Present or last known position, flight level/altitude and heading;

(h) Pilot qualifications (See Note 1), viz:
    (i) Student pilots (see Note 2);
    (ii) No Instrument Qualification;
    (iii) IMC Rating;
    (iv) Full Instrument Rating.

(j) Any other useful information eg endurance remaining, number of people on board (POB) etc.

Notes:

1   There is no ICAO requirement to include pilot qualifications in an emergency message. However, this information should be included whenever possible in UK emergency messages as it may help the controller to plan a course of action best suited to the pilot's ability.

2   Inexperienced civil pilots are invited to use the callsign prefix 'TYRO' when in communication with a military unit or the D&D Section to indicate their lack of experience. Upon hearing this code word, military controllers will ensure that they do not issue complex instructions which the pilot could have difficulty in following.

Mayday mayday mayday Milthorpe Tower G-ABCD Slingsby engine fire losing height intend an immediate forced landing 20 miles south of Milthorpe. Passing 3000 feet heading 360 PPL 1 POB	G-ABCD Milthorpe Tower roger mayday ..... (any pertinent information)
Mayday mayday mayday Milthorpe Tower G-ABCD C172 engine failed. Will attempt to land Milthorpe, 10 miles south, 4000 ft heading 360 Student pilot	G-ABCD Milthorpe Tower roger mayday cleared straight-in runway 35 wind 260 10 knots QFE 1008 you are number one

9.6   SPEECHLESS CODE

9.6.1   If an emergency message received by the Military Emergency Controller is weak or distorted to the point of being unintelligible, the pilot may be asked to adopt the Speechless Code. This entails the pilot pressing his transmit button a certain number of times and using carrier wave only transmissions which, by convention, have the following code meanings:

Number of transmissions	Meaning
One Short	'Yes' or an acknowledgement
Two Short	'No'
Three Short	'Say again' (to be used by the pilot when he has not fully heard the controller's transmission, or has not understood the transmission, or the transmission was an instruction and the pilot is unable to comply).
Four Short (letter H in morse)	'Request Homing' (to an airfield), or used for initial alerting. (A civil pilot should only use the four short transmissions if he is aware, or suspects before attempting to make initial contact with the Emergency Controller, that his own aircraft microphone is unserviceable. The Emergency Controller will then interrogate the pilot, using the callsign 'Speechless Aircraft' if the identity of the aircraft is unknown).
One Long (2 secs)	'Manoeuvre Complete' (eg steady on heading).
One Long, Two Short and One Long (–..–) (letter X in morse)	'My aircraft has developed another emergency'

9.6.2   An aircraft SSR transponder can also be used, during times of communication difficulties, by a pilot to acknowledge or respond to messages by the transmission of SSR Code changes or squawking 'Ident' as requested by the controller.

9.6.3   If neither the state of DISTRESS nor URGENCY applies, an emergency service is available at lower priority to pilots who find themselves in DIFFICULTY. Such pilots should make their situation clear and then provide as much information as possible to the emergency controller from the list at para 9.5.3 (a) to (j).

9.7   RADIO PROCEDURES – PRACTICE EMERGENCIES

9.7.1   Pilots may simulate emergency incidents (BUT NOT THE STATE OF DISTRESS) on 121.50 MHz to enable them to gain experience of the ATC service provided. Before calling, pilots should listen out on the emergency frequency to ensure that no actual or practice incident is already in progress. Practice calls need not disrupt a planned flight or involve additional expense in fuel or time since the pilot can request 'diversion' to his intended destination or cancel the exercise when necessary. Simulated emergency calls must be prefixed 'PRACTICE' and should be brief, eg:

> 'PRACTICE PAN, PRACTICE PAN, PRACTICE PAN,
> LONDON CENTRE THIS IS G-ABCD'

The Emergency Controller will then indicate acceptance of the Practice Pan by transmitting:

> G-ABCD, THIS IS LONDON CENTRE CONTINUE
> WITH PRACTICE PAN'

The Emergency Controller may instruct the pilot to call at another time, if the practice cannot be accommodated.

9.7.2   If a practice is accepted, the pilot should then pass his details. SSR Mode A Code 7700 should *not* be selected during a practice emergency exercise unless required by the Emergency Controller. Mode C should be switched on, if available.

9.8   RELAYED EMERGENCY MESSAGE

9.8.1   Any aeronautical station or aircraft knowing of an emergency incident may transmit a distress message whenever such action is necessary to obtain assistance for the aircraft or vessel in distress. In such circumstances, it should be made clear that the aircraft transmitting is not itself in distress.

> Mayday mayday mayday
> Milthorpe Tower G-ABCD
> have intercepted mayday
> from G-BJRD I say again
> G-BJRD Cessna 172 engine
> failure forced landing 10
> miles west of Wicken VOR,   G-ABCD Milthorpe Tower
> 1000 feet descending,   roger your relayed mayday
> heading 120, PPL, over   from G-BJRD

9.9   IMPOSITION OF SILENCE

9.9.1   Transmissions from aircraft in emergency have priority over all other transmissions. On hearing an emergency call, all stations must maintain radio silence on that frequency unless they themselves are required to render assistance and should continue to listen on the frequency concerned until it is evident that assistance is being provided (see 9.6.1).

9.9.2   The aircraft in emergency or the station in control of an emergency incident may impose silence either on all stations in the area or on any particular station that interferes with emergency transmissions. In either case, the message should take the following form:

> All stations Milthorpe Tower
> stop transmitting. Mayday

> or

> G-ABCD stop transmitting.
> Mayday

9.9.3 The aeronautical station acknowledging a emergency message on a particular frequency may consider it prudent to transfer other aircraft from that frequency in order to avoid any disruption of transmission from or to the emergency aircraft.

> Mayday G-BJRD all other
> aircraft contact Milthorpe
> Tower on 123.8

9.10 CANCELLATION OF EMERGENCY COMMUNICATIONS AND RTF SILENCE

9.10.1 When an aircraft is no longer in emergency it shall transmit a message cancelling the emergency condition.

> Milthorpe Tower G-BJRD
> cancel mayday, engine
> restarted, runway in sight.
> Request landing

> G-RD cleared to land
> runway 35. Surface wind
> 320 6

> Cleared to land runway 35
> G-RD

9.10.2 When an emergency incident has been resolved, the station which has been controlling the emergency traffic will transmit a message indicating that normal working may be resumed.

> All stations Milthorpe Tower
> mayday traffic ended

CHAPTER 10 – TRANSMISSION OF AERODROME INFORMATION

10.1 METEOROLOGICAL INFORMATION

10.1.1 Meteorological information in the form of reports, forecasts or warnings is made available to pilots using the aeronautical mobile service either by broadcast (eg VOLMET) or by means of specific transmissions from ground personnel to pilots. Standard meteorological abbreviations and terms should be used and the information should be transmitted slowly and enunciated clearly in order that the recipient may record such data as is necessary.

> G-CD Borton Tower 0950
> weather surface wind
> 360 degrees 5 knots visibility
> 30 kms. Nil weather, 2 oktas
> 25000 feet temperature
> plus 10, dew point plus 3,
> QNH 1010   QNH 1010 G-CD

10.2 VOICE WEATHER BROADCAST (VOLMET) UK

10.2.1 Meteorological aerodrome reports for certain aerodromes are broadcast on specified frequencies. The callsign of the VOLMET, frequency, operating hours, aerodromes contained within thegroup, and contents are published in the UK AIP.

10.2.2 The content of a VOLMET broadcast is as follows:

(a)   Aerodrome identification (eg Stourton)

(b)   Surface wind

(c)   Visibility (Note 1)

(d)   RVR (if applicable) (Note 1)

(e)   Weather

(f)   Cloud (Note 1)

(g)   Temperature

(h)   Dewpoint

(i)   QNH

(j)   Trend (if applicable)

Notes: 1   Non essential words such as 'surface wind', 'visibility' etc
            are not spoken.
        2   'SNOCLO' is used to indicate that aerodrome is unusable
            for take-off/landings due to heavy snow on runways or
            snow clearance.
        3   All broadcasts are in English.

10.3   RUNWAY VISUAL RANGE (RVR)

10.3.1   When transmitting the runway visual range the abbreviation RVR will
         be used without using the phonetic word for each letter, eg RVR
         runway 27, 800 metres. The runway designator may be omitted if there
         is no possibility of confusion.

10.3.2   Where instrumented runway visual range (IRVR) observations are
         available, more than one reading may be transmitted.

Fastair 345 RVR runway 27
650 600 600   Fastair 345

Fastair 345 RVR runway 27
touchdown 650 stop end 550   Fastair 345

10.4   RUNWAY SURFACE CONDITIONS

10.4.1   When conditions of standing water, with or without reports of braking
         action, are brought to the attention of a controller, the available
         information will be passed to aircraft likely to be affected.

10.4.2   Information on standing water will be passed in general descriptive terms, for example 'damp', 'wet', 'water patches' or 'flooded' according to the amount of water present.

10.4.3   When suitable equipment is available reports of braking action on wet runways will be passed to pilots.

10.4.4   Other runway surface conditions which may be of concern to a pilot will be passed by ATC.

Fastair 345 braking action medium, heavy rain time of measurement 0830	Fastair 345
Fastair 345 displaced threshold runway 27 500 feet due broken surface	Fastair 345

10.5   AUTOMATIC TERMINAL INFORMATION SERVICE (ATIS) UK

10.5.1   To alleviate RTF loading at some busy airports, Automatic Terminal Information Service (ATIS) messages are broadcast to pass routine arrival/departure information on a discrete RTF frequency or on an appropriate VOR. Pilots inbound to these airports are normally required on first contact with the aerodrome ATSU to acknowledge receipt of current information by quoting the code letter of the broadcast. Pilots of outbound aircraft are not normally required to acknowledge receipt of departure ATIS except when requested on the actual ATIS broadcast.

10.5.2   Aerodromes possessing ATIS, the hours of ATIS operation and the frequency employed are published in the UK AIP.

10.5.3   ATIS broadcasts will include the following:

(a)   Message identification ie 'This is Stourton Information Alpha'. Each message is consecutively coded using the phonetic alphabet.

(b)   Time of origin of weather report.

(c)   Weather report (see para 10.2.2(a)–(c)).

(d)   Runway(s) in use.

(e)   Short term AIS information such as unserviceability of NAV AIDS, runway surfaces etc.

(f)   Any other routine information useful to pilots operating at the aerodrome.

Notes: 1 The QFE and RVR/RVRs are not included.
         2 Rapidly changing meteorological situations sometimes make it impractical to include weather reports in the broadcast. In these circumstances, ATIS messages will indicate that weather information will be passed on RTF.
         3 Any significant change to the content of a current ATIS message will be passed to pilots by RTF until such time as a new message is broadcast.
         4 The highest cloud base that will be reported is 10000 feet.

10.5.4   Example of ATIS broadcast:

'This is Stourton Information Alpha. 0850 hours weather. 240° 12 kts. 10 km. Intermittent slight rain. 3 octas 1000 ft, 8 octas 1800 ft. Temperature +12. Dew point +7. QNH 1011 mbs. Landing runway 28. Report information Alpha received on first contact with Stourton.'

CHAPTER 11 – MISCELLANEOUS FLIGHT HANDLING

11.1   WAKE TURBULENCE

11.1.1   When wake turbulence is suspected or known to exist ATC will warn aircraft as appropriate. Normally ATC will provide the spacing between aircraft but, if a pilot elects to execute a visual approach, or is operating as a VFR flight, it is his responsibility for adequate spacing, although ATC will pass the appropriate distance.

> G-BJCD caution vortex wake
> the recommended spacing is
> ..... miles
>
> G-BJCD

11.2   WIND SHEAR

11.2.1   When wind shear is forecast or is reported by aircraft, ATC will warn other aircraft until such time as aircraft report the phenomenon no longer exists.

> G-CD at 0745 a departing
> B757 reported windshear at
> 800 feet. Airspeed loss 20 kts,
> strong right drift

11.3   AIRMISS REPORTING

11.3.1   An Airmiss Report should be made by any pilot flying in the United Kingdom Flight Information Region, the Upper Flight Information Region or Shanwick Oceanic Area when he considers that his aircraft may have been endangered during the flight by the proximity of another aircraft to the extent that a risk of collision existed.

11.3.2   The initial report is made by RTF to the ATSU in communication with the aircraft except that if the controllers workload is such that he is not able to accept the report the pilot will be requested to file details after landing.

11.3.3   The Pilot's RTF report should commence with words 'AIRMISS REPORT' and should include the following items:

Aircraft Callsign

SSR Code

Position of airmiss

Aircraft heading

Flight level, altitude or height

Altimeter setting

Aircraft attitude (level/climbing/descending/turning)

Weather conditions

Date and time (UTC) of the Airmiss

Description of other aircraft

First sighting distance and details of flight paths of reporting and reported aircraft.

11.3.4   RTF Airmiss reports are to be confirmed in writing within seven days of the incident to allow follow up action to be taken. (See UK AIP RAC Section.)

11.4   OIL POLLUTION REPORTING

11.4.1   Pilots sighting substantial patches of oil are requested to make reports by RTF to the ATSU with whom they are in communication or the appropriate FIS in order that action can be taken.

The RTF reports should contain the following:

'OIL POLLUTION REPORT' OR 'POLLUTION REPORT'

. . . Time and date (if required) pollution was observed and identify of reporting aircraft.
. . . Position and extent of pollution
. . . Tide, windspeed and direction
. . . Weather conditions and Sea state
. . . Characteristics of pollution

... Name and nationality or description, including any distinctive markings, of any vessel seen discharging oil or other harmful substances; also estimated course and speed of vessel and if pollution is observed ahead of the discharging ship and the estimated length of pollution in her wake

... Identity of any other vessels in the immediate vicinity

... Whether photographs taken.

11.5 INTERCEPTIONS BY MILITARY AIRCRAFT – RTF

Pilots are warned that should they become involved in an interception by military aircraft they should follow the international procedures as detailed in the UK AIP RAC Section.

11.6 AIRCRAFT OPERATING AGENCY MESSAGES

11.6.1 Aircraft operating agency radio stations may only transmit and receive flight regularity and flight safety messages.

11.6.2 Flight regularity messages comprise the following:

(a) Messages regarding the operation or maintenance of facilities essential for the safety or regularity of aircraft operation.

(b) Messages concerning the servicing of aircraft.

(c) Instructions to aircraft operating agency representatives concerning changes in requirements for passengers and crew caused by unavoidable deviations from normal operating schedules. Individual requirements of passengers or crew are not admissible in this type of message.

(d) Messages concerning non-routine landings to be made by the aircraft.

(e) Messages concerning aircraft parts and materials urgently required.

(f) Messages concerning changes in aircraft operating schedules.

11.6.3   Flight safety messages include the following:

(a)   Messages originated by an aircraft operating agency, or by an aircraft, of immediate concern to an aircraft in flight.

(b)   Meteorological advice of immediate concern to an aircraft in flight or about to depart.

11.6.4   It is permissible for aircraft operating agency messages to be handled by the aerodrome communication facility provided this can be achieved without interference with its primary role and no other channels are available for the handling of such messages.

11.6.5   Public correspondence messages are not permitted on frequencies in the aeronautical mobile service.

CHAPTER 12 – EXAMPLES OF AN IFR FLIGHT AND A VFR FLIGHT

12.1   INTRODUCTION

12.1.1   An example of an IFR flight from one major airport to another, and an example of a VFR flight from a provincial aerodrome to a landing site, are given in graphic form in this chapter. As before the agency making the initial call is on the left-hand side of the page; thereafter messages connected with the subject appear in colour-coded chronological order but on the *relative* side of the page. The agencies can be identified as follows:

FASTAIR 345

G-ABCD

GROUND/TOWER/APPROACH

WRAYTON ATCC (CONTROL/INFORMATION)

12.2 THE IFR FLIGHT

12.2.1 Start up

Stourton Ground Fastair 345 radio check 118.3

Station calling Stourton Ground say again your callsign

Stourton Ground Fastair 345. Radio check 118.3

Fastair 345 Stourton Ground readability 5.

Ground Fastair 345, stand 24, information bravo, request start up

Fastair 345 start up *approved*

Note: APPROVED used-not CLEAR/CLEARED.

12.2.2 Clearance

Fastair 345 is *cleared* from Stourton to Kennington via A1 at FL 60, request level change en-route, squawk 5501

Cleared from Stourton to Kennington at FL 60, request level change en-route, squawk 5501 Fastair 345

Fastair 345 correct

Notes: 1 The word CLEARED is introduced – see para 12.2.4.
2 A full readback of a clearance is required.

12.2.3 Pushback and Taxi

Ground Fastair 345 request pushback

Fastair 345 pushback *approved*

Note: APPROVED – NOT CLEAR

Ground Fastair 345 information charlie request taxi

Fastair 345 taxi to holding point runway 24

Taxi to holding point runway 24 Fastair 345

Fastair 345 contact Stourton Tower 118.9

Stourton Tower 118.9 Fastair 345

Note: Full readback of taxi clearance as the message contains the runway in use – see para 2.7.5.5.

12.2.4 Pre-departure and Take-off

Stourton Tower Fastair 345 ready for *departure*

Fastair 345 Stourton Tower after *departure* climb straight ahead until passing 2500 feet

After *departure* climb straight ahead until passing 2500 feet Fastair 345

Fastair 345 *line up and wait. Vehicle crossing upwind end of runway*

Line up and wait. Fastair 345

Notes: 1   'DEPARTURE' employed and not 'TAKE-OFF'.
2   'CLEARED' is not used in these cases – see below.
3   Full readback is required for instructions to ENTER, LAND, TAKE-OFF ON, BACKTRACK, HOLD SHORT OF, OR CROSS a runway.
4   'LINE UP AND WAIT' (plus reason) is employed; 'LINE UP' (only) may also be used.

| Fastair 345 cleared take-off surface wind calm | Cleared take-off Fastair 345 |

Notes: 1 TAKE-OFF – these words are *only* used when an aircraft is cleared for TAKE-OFF.
    2 TAKE-OFF clearance requires readback.
    3 Use of CLEAR is restricted to:
        (i)   ATC clearances.
        (ii)   Departure and Approach instructions.
        (iii) Take-off and landing clearances.

Fastair 345 contact Wrayton Control 129.1

Wrayton Control 129.1 Fastair 345

Note: Full readback of frequency change.

12.2.5 En-Route

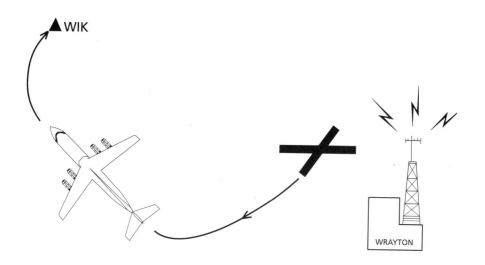

Wrayton Control Fastair 345 passing 3000 feet turning inbound Wicken climbing FL 60 requesting FL 280

Fastair 345 Wrayton Control climb report reaching FL 280

Climbing FL 280 Wilco Fastair 345

Notes: 1 Full readback of level instruction.
2 REPORT instruction employed.

WRAYTON

Fastair 345 Wicken 47 FL 130
climbing FL 280 Marlow 07

Fastair 345 roger

Note: Position report consists of:

(a) Aircraft identification.
(b) Position.
(c) Time.
(d) Level.
(e) Next position and ETA.

▲ MAR

WRAYTON

| Fastair 345 FL 280 | Fastair 345 |

Note: For passing instructions/reports regarding height/altitude or flight level, use CLIMB, DESCEND, PASSING, REACHING or LEAVING but *not* CLEARED/RE-CLEARED.

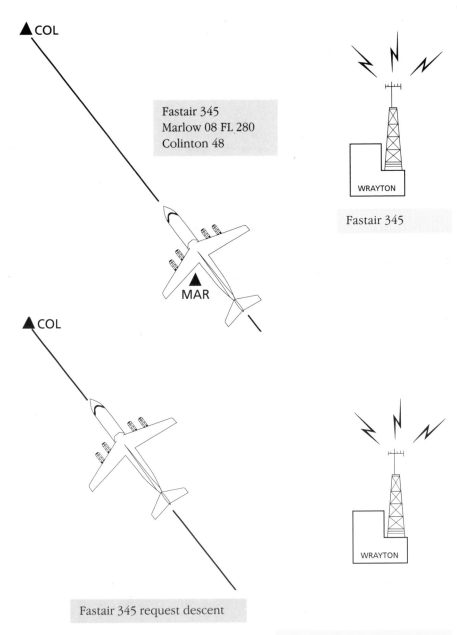

Fastair 345
Marlow 08 FL 280
Colinton 48

Fastair 345

Fastair 345 request descent

Fastair 345 descend FL 120
cross Colinton FL 170 or
above

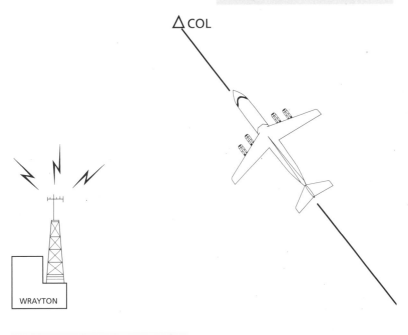

Descending FL 120 will cross
Colinton FL 170 or above
Fastair 345

△COL

WRAYTON

Fastair 345 report your level

Fastair 345 passing FL 225

Fastair 345 roger. Are you
able to cross Colinton at time
52

Affirm. Fastair 345

Fastair 345 cross Colinton not
before time 52

Cross Colinton not before 52
Fastair 345

Note: AFFIRM(ative)/NEGATIVE are used when a question requires a
direct answer. Therefore, ROGER is not used in this case.

Fastair 345 Colinton 52
FL 180 descending FL 120
request direct North Cross
for ILS approach at
Kennington

Fastair 345 roger. Route
direct to North Cross.
Descend FL 60. Report west
abeam KTN

Direct North Cross
descending FL 60. Wilco
Fastair 345

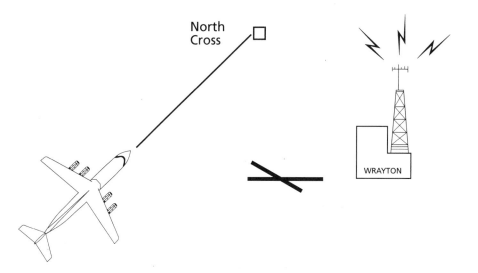

Fastair 345 West abeam
Kennington 03 FL 110
descending FL 60 North
Cross at 11

Fastair 345 roger. Contact
Kennington Approach 119.7

Kennington Approach 119.7
Fastair 345

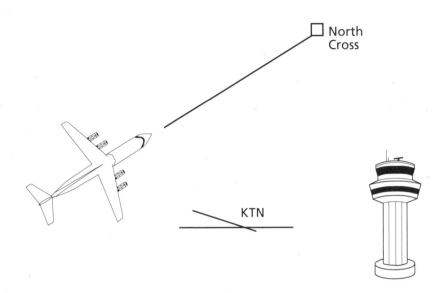

Kennington Approach Fastair
345 FL 90 descending FL 60
approaching North Cross
information Golf

Fastair 345 Kennington
Approach vectoring for ILS
approach runway 28

ILS RW 28 QNH 1011
Fastair 345

Fastair 345 Leave North
Cross heading 120

Leave North Cross heading
120 Fastair 345

Note: Full readback of HEADING (and speed) instructions; also
runway identifier.

North
Cross

Fastair 345 North Cross FL 60
heading 120

Fastair 345 descend to
altitude 2500 feet QNH 1011

Descending to altitude 2500
feet QNH 1011
Fastair 345

Fastair 345 position 10 miles
northeast of Kennington

Fastair 345

Fastair 345 turn right
heading 190 base leg
14 miles northeast of
Kennington

Right heading 190 Fastair 345

Fastair 345 turn right heading 240

Right heading 240 Fastair 345

Fastair 345 closing final approach track from the right 12 miles from touchdown

Fastair 345

Fastair 345 closing the localiser from the right, report established

Wilco Fastair 345

Fastair 345 localiser established

Fastair 345 descend on the ILS QFE 1008

QFE 1008, wilco Fastair 345

Fastair 345 contact Tower 118.9

Tower 118.9 Fastair 345

Kennington Tower
Fastair 345 long final RW 28

Fastair 345 Kennington Tower
cleared to land runway 28
surface wind 240 10

Cleared to land runway 28
Fastair 345

Note: Surface wind: 'Degrees' and 'Knots' may be omitted.

Fastair 345 *vacate*
convenient right

Vacate right Fastair 345

Fastair 345 runway *vacated*

Note: VACATE runway and *not* CLEAR runway.

143

12.3   A VFR FLIGHT

12.3.1   This particular example is aimed at the pilot flying outside regulated airspace under services provided by the military in the UK (Westbury) to show the slight differences that exist from civil ATS as portrayed in previous chapters.

12.3.2   **Engine Start and Departure Information**

Borton Tower G-ABCD radio check 118.7	G-ABCD Borton Tower loud and clear
Borton Tower G-ABCD Slingsby T67 starting, request departure information	G-CD departure runway 24 surface wind 220 6, QNH 1010 temperature +6 dew point +3
Runway 24 QNH 1012 G-CD	G-CD negative. QNH 1010
QNH 1010 G-CD	
Borton Tower G-ABCD, T67 at the south side hangars request taxi for VFR flight to Walden	G-CD taxy to holding point runway 24 via taxiway Charlie QNH 1010
Holding point runway 24 via taxiway Charlie QNH 1010, request surface wind G-CD	G-CD surface wind calm
G-CD request departure on runway 14	G-CD taxy to holding point runway 14
Taxy to holding point runway 14 G-CD	

12.3.3 Pre-departure and Take-off

G-CD ready for *departure* request left turnout heading 330

G-CD, left turn *approved*. After departure climb not above altitude 2500 feet until reaching the zone boundary

Left turn approved. Not above altitude 2500 feet until zone boundary G-CD

G-CD cleared take-off runway 14 surface wind 220 4

Cleared take-off runway 14 G-CD

Notes: 1 DEPARTURE used not TAKE-OFF.
2 APPROVED used not CLEARED.
3 Full readback of departure clearance.
4 Runway identified as in this case it is not the runway in use.
5 Readback of take-off clearance.

12.3.4 Post Departure

G-CD contact Borton
Approach 118.75

Borton Approach 118.75
G-CD

Borton Approach G-ABCD
airborne runway 14 turning
left heading 330 climbing to
altitude 2500 feet, en-route
Walden

G-CD roger *report* reaching
2500 feet

G-CD wilco

G-CD maintaining altitude
2500 feet

G-CD roger *report* at the
zone boundary

Wilco G-CD

G-CD zone boundary
changing to Wrayton
Information 125.75

G-CD roger, Regional
QNH 1008

Regional QNH 1008 G-CD

Notes: 1   REPORT introduced.
       2   CHANGING TO announces intention to change frequency.

146

12.3.5 **En-route**

WRAYTON

Wrayton Information
G-ABCD request Flight
Information Service

G-ABCD Wrayton
Information pass your
message

Wrayton G-ABCD T67
15 miles northwest of Borton
heading 330, climbing FL 45,
VFR destination Walden

G-CD roger. Flight
Information Service

G-CD Flight Information,
maintaining FL 45

G-CD

Wrayton G-CD request VHF
frequency for Westbury
Approach

G-CD Westbury Approach
119.7

Wrayton Information G-CD
descending due weather.
Changing to Westbury
Approach for LARS

G-CD regional QNH 1008

Regional QNH 1008 G-CD

12.3.4 Lower Airspace Radar Service and MATZ Penetration Service

Note: Westbury is a military unit.

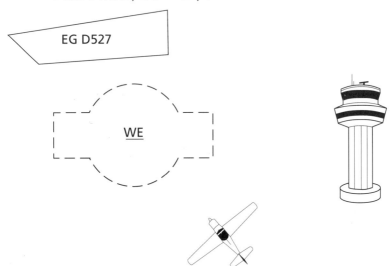

Westbury Approach G-ABCD request Lower Airspace Radar Service

G-CD Westbury Approach pass your message

Westbury G-CD Slingsby T67 20 miles southeast of Westbury, heading 340, FL 40 descending to altitude 2500 feet regional QNH 1008, VFR en-route Walden requesting Radar Advisory Service

G-CD squawk 6512

6512 G-CD

G-CD identified 16 miles southeast of Westbury. Radar Advisory. Report reaching 2500 feet

Radar Advisory, wilco. G-CD request MATZ penetration

G-CD roger

Note: Details of LARS and MATZ Penetration Service can be found in the UK AIP, AICs and Temporary Supplements.

EG D527

WE

G-CD request level

G-CD altitude 2900 feet

EG D527

WE

G-CD set Westbury
QNH 1009

Westbury QNH 1009 set G-CD

G-CD descend report level
1500 feet for MATZ
penetration

Descend report level altitude
1500 feet G-CD

G-CD maintaining 1500 feet

G-CD maintain 1500 feet
MATZ penetration approved

MATZ penetration approved
G-CD

Note: Military controllers do not apply the conventions relating to the
        use of altitude/height clearances as described at para 3.2.3(b).

G-CD entering MATZ limited
warning of traffic from ahead
as you approach my radar
overhead

G-CD roger. Request join for
one visual circuit

G-CD roger. Standby

G-CD one visual circuit
approved maintain 1500 ft to
overhead. Do you have the
field in sight?

Maintain 1500 ft to overhead.
G-CD has the field in sight

G-CD roger. Runway 27 right
hand circuit height 1000 feet
QFE 1001

Runway 27 right hand circuit
height 1000 feet QFE 1001
G-CD

G-CD what is your POB

G-CD 1 POB

G-CD contact Westbury
Tower 132.85, radar service
terminated

Westbury Tower 132.85 G-CD

Notes: 1   The question of landing fees etc is not addressed in this
            scenario.
        2   Circuit direction is only given when circuit is not left-
            hand.
        3   Military units now employ QFE in the circuit area.

12.3.5 **The Military Visual Circuit**

Westbury Tower G-ABCD
2 miles southeast height
1500 ft QFE 1001 to join for
one visual circuit

G-CD Westbury Tower join
overhead at 1500 feet for
runway 27 right hand QFE
1001 circuit clear

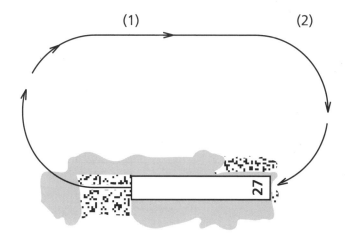

Join overhead 1500 feet
runway 27 right hand
QFE 1001 G-CD

G-CD overhead 1500 feet

G-CD report downwind at
1000 feet one fast jet joining
base leg to land

Wilco G-CD

(1)   (2)

Military Rectangular Visual Circuit Pattern

Notes: 1   Downwind report is made abeam upwind end of runway.
            Aircraft intentions are stated here.
        2   'Finals' call is made *just before turning base leg*.
        3   Military (jet) circuits tend to be relatively tight and are
            more oval-shaped.

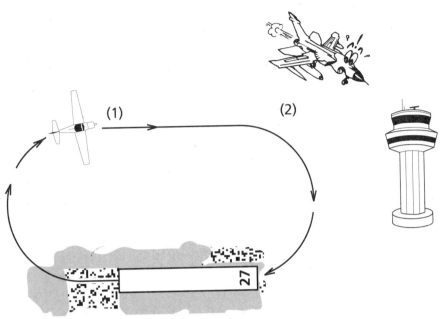

(1)

G-CD downwind 1000 feet
request touch and go then
depart to the northwest.
Request Danger Area
Crossing Service of EGD512

G-CD surface wind 250 5 one
ahead to land. DACS request
copied

(2)

G-CD final gear down

G-CD go around 500 feet
deadside one on remaining

Go around 500 ft deadside
G-CD

Notes: 1 Surface wind is passed at downwind position.
        2 An aircraft with retractable undercarriage will be expected
           to call 'gear down' or three greens with the final call.

G-CD at upwind end of runway turn right heading 290 climb to 2000 feet QNH 1009

Upwind end of runway right heading 290 climb to altitude 2000 feet QNH 1009 G-CD

G-CD heading 290 climbing to altitude 2000 feet

G-CD contact Westbury Approach 119.7

Westbury Approach 119.7 G-CD

Note: Full readback of clearance and frequency change.

Westbury Approach G-ABCD
heading 290 maintaining
altitude 2000 ft QNH 1009

G-CD Westbury Approach
squawk ident

Ident G-CD

G-CD identified, Radar
Advisory, EGD512 Loudwater
active will you accept a
re-route

Radar Advisory, affirm G-CD

G-CD maintain heading 290
what is your requested level

Heading 290 request FL 45

G-CD climb FL 45

Climbing FL 45 G-CD

Notes: 1   AFFIRM used.
      2   Military controllers use 'MAINTAIN' heading.

EG D527

WE

G-CD leaving MATZ

G-CD

G-CD maintaining FL 45

G-CD roger I will be turning you right in 7 miles to regain track

G-CD

Note: Report leaving a MATZ.

12.3.7 **Avoiding Action**

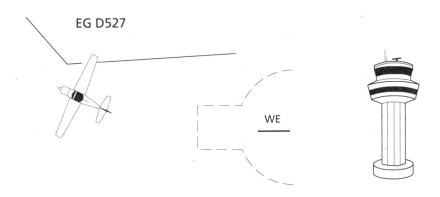

EG D527

WE

G-CD avoiding action, turn left heading 230 pop-up traffic was left 11 o'clock range 6 miles no height reciprocal heading

Left heading 230 G-CD

Notes: 1 This type of avoiding action when under Radar Advisory is given at the controller's discretion for late sighting/pop-up traffic.

2 Normally an avoiding action call as follows can be expected: G-CD traffic left 11 o'clock 6 miles height unknown crossing left to right, if not sighted turn left heading 230.

EG D527

WE

G-CD clear of traffic, turn right heading 340 direct for Walden

Right heading 340. Request change to Wrayton Information 125.75 G-CD

G-CD squawk Alpha 7000 Westbury terminating service

Alpha 7000 G-CD

12.3.10 En-Route/Flight Information Service

EG D527

WRAYTON

Wrayton Information
G-ABCD request Flight
Information Service

G-ABCD Wrayton Information
pass your message

Wrayton Information G-ABCD
T67 15 miles northwest of
Westbury heading 340, FL 45,
VFR, en-route Walden,
request Walden weather

G-CD roger Flight
Information Service, standby
for weather

Flight Information, G-CD

G-CD I have the Walden
weather are you ready to
copy

Affirm G-CD

G-CD Walden 0950 weather
runway 27, surface wind calm,
visibility 10 kilometres, nil
weather, 3 octas at 4000,
QNH 1009 temperature +4.
Dew point +1

G-CD changing to Wrayton
on 121.5 for Practice PAN

G-CD

12.3.11 **Practice Pan**

(121.5 – listen out before transmitting)

Practice Pan, Practice Pan,
Practice Pan, Wrayton Centre
this is G-ABCD

G-ABCD this is Wrayton
Centre continue with Practice
Pan

Wrayton Centre G-ABCD,
Slingsby T67, simulating
rough running engine,
request diversion to nearest
aerodrome, 20 miles
northwest of Westbury, FL
45, turning right heading
140, IMC rating, one person
on board squawking Alpha
7000 with Charlie

G-ABCD Wrayton squawk
7301 ident

7301 ident G-ABCD

EG D

G-ABCD identified 17 miles northwest of Westbury, turn right heading 160 for Westbury for landing runway 09 surface wind 270 3 knots

Heading 160 for approach to runway 09 at Westbury G-ABCD

G-ABCD are you ready for Westbury weather, 13 miles northwest of Westbury

Wrayton Westbury weather not required cancelling Practice Pan G-ABCD

G-ABCD roger. Practice Pan cancelled

G-ABCD changing to Walden 135.25

G-ABCD squawk A-7000

A-7000 G-ABCD

Note: Use of the VHF International Emergency Service is detailed in the UK AIP and AICs and Chapter 9.

12.3.12 **Arrival**

Walden Information G-ABCD inbound

> G-CD Walden Information runway 27 QFE 1006 pass your message

G-ABCD T67, 6 miles southeast descending to height 1000 feet QFE 1006.

> G-CD 3 aircraft in circuit

3 aircraft in circuit. Joining left base G-CD

> G-CD

G-CD final

> G-CD one aircraft on runway vacating. Land at your discretion, surface wind 260 6

G-CD contact

G-CD runway vacated

G-ABCD

Our thanks to Squadron Leader M J Setterfield RAF for the cartoons.

BIBLIOGRAPHY

Titles

Books referred to in this publication are as follows:

ICAO Annex 10 Volume 2 – COMMUNICATION PROCEDURES
Reference No. 9031   Price £5.35

PANS-RAC Document 4444: PROCEDURES FOR AIR NAVIGATION SERVICES –
RULES OF THE AIR AND AIR TRAFFIC SERVICES
Reference No. 4444   Price £18.44

UK AIP (CAP 32): UNITED KINGDOM AERONAUTICAL INFORMATION
PUBLICATION   All 'RAC' references are contained herein
Reference No. 0031   Price £350.00

MATS Part 1 (CAP 493): MANUAL OF AIR TRAFFIC SERVICES PART 1
Reference No. 7506   Price £30.00

MAFIS (CAP 410): MANUAL OF AERODROME FLIGHT INFORMATION SERVICES
Reference No. 7107   Price £6.80

Operators Guide (CAP 452): AERONAUTICAL RADIO STATION –
OPERATORS' GUIDE
Reference No. 0452   Price £1.50

NOTE: The above prices are valid until 31 December 1992. After that date the
prices should be obtained by telephoning the number shown overleaf.

Methods of purchase

CAA and ICAO publications may be obtained from CAA Printing and Publication
Services (P&PS) by the following methods:

Post – Use Order Form at the end of the book or write order detailing reference
no. (this is a code system directly relating to computer ordering), publication
details, quantity required and cost per item(s). Add post and packing charges
plus VAT where applicable, and advise the method of payment to be used. (Most
of the amendment subscription services are inclusive of postage and packing.)

Telephone – Orders are accepted by telephone at P&PS Cheltenham (0242) 235151. Where payment is to be made by cheque then a written confirmation order must be sent together with the cheque.

Fax – Order forms or written orders are acceptable by fax at P&PS, Cheltenham (0242) 584139; but payment must be received before goods are despatched.

Proforma – In cases where costs are unknown or the request is not properly completed, a proforma may be raised detailing correct information and monies due before the order can proceed.

Cheques – Cheques to be made payable to Civil Aviation Authority (written in full).

Credit Cards – Visa and Access credit cards are acceptable, also Switch for personal callers only. An order paid by this method may be by post, telephone or fax to P&PS. A new dedicated telephone line is now available *for credit card transactions only* Cheltenham (0242) 263993.

International Money Order – For overseas customers payment in sterling by International Money Order or Bank Draft drawn on a UK bank is required.

Personal callers – Personal callers are welcome to make purchases (by arrangement only). Please telephone to ensure that required publications are available as stocks may need to be obtained from our warehouse first and the method of payment agreed before goods can be collected. (See Publication Order Form at end of book for telephone number and address.)

INDEX

(Does not encompass Chapter 12)

PUBLICATIONS ORDER FORM

Please supply the following publications:

REFERENCE NO.	DESCRIPTION	UNIT PRICE	QUANTITY	TOTAL PRICE
	PACKING AND POSTAGE			
	VAT (if applicable)			
	GRAND TOTAL			

CUSTOMER INFORMATION Please use BLOCK CAPITALS

Name _____

Address _____

_____

_____

Postcode _____ Daytime Tel No. _____

Signature _____ Date _____

POSTAGE AND PACKING RATES

	UK	Overseas (surface)
Order up to £3 in value (including free of charge publications)	£0.60	£ 1.60
over £3 up to £6	£1.20	£ 2.20
over £6 up to £10	£1.90	£ 2.75
over £10 up to £20	£3.60	£ 5.50
over £20 up to £50	£4.80	£ 7.20
over £50 up to £100	£7.40	£11.00

Orders over £100 will be subject to special rates depending on number of packages and costs involved.
VAT is applicable to the Postage and Packing charges where the goods supplied are Standard Rated.

METHOD OF PAYMENT

(a) Remittance for £ _____ is enclosed (Cheque/Postal Order/Money Order payable to Civil Aviation Authority).

ACCESS or VISA only

(b) Please debit my credit card no: ☐☐☐☐☐☐☐☐☐☐☐☐☐☐☐ expiry date ☐☐☐☐

(c) Telephone orders may be made to CREDIT CARD HOTLINE – Cheltenham (0242) 263993. This form submitted as confirmation only.

(d) Overseas customers are requested to pay by a sterling draft drawn on a UK Bank or International Money Order in sterling.

Please ensure all parts of this Order Form have been completed correctly and despatch to:

Civil Aviation Authority, Printing and Publication Services, Greville House, 37 Gratton Road, Cheltenham, Glos. GL50 2BN, England. Telephone Cheltenham (0242) 235151.